the collected cathy

by Cathy Guisewite

A 2-in-1 Volume including: **Another Saturday night of wild and reckless abandon** and **A mouthful of breath mints and no one to kiss**

Two Cathys — I suppose we all could use a couple of Cathys in our lives. The Cathy in Cathy Guisewite's strip is really not the Cathy Guisewite I know. I can tell them apart with no trouble at all.

The comic strip "Cathy" points out for us just how much trouble life is for a young working girl. She shrieks in agony, laughs with delight, and works very hard. I don't know if Cathy Guisewite ever shrieks in agony, but I know she laughs easily, and works very hard. It is not really difficult, in spite of what you may have heard, to draw a comic strip every day, but it is very, very difficult to make it better and better, and this is what Cathy Guisewite has been doing. "Cathy" gets better every day.

I like having two Cathys in my life!

—Charles M. Schulz
Creator of "Peanuts"

Another Saturday night of wild and reckless abandon

by Cathy Guisewite

Andrews and McMeel, Inc.
A Universal Press Syndicate Company

Kansas City ● New York

A  collection

YOU'RE TOO GOOD FOR IRVING, CATHY.

YEAH, I KNOW...

I'M TOO GOOD FOR EMERSON, TOO.

HA! I'M ALSO TOO GOOD FOR RICHARD, PHILLIP, TOM, STEVE, GREG, HENRY, BILL, MARK, BRIAN, TIM, JOHN, BOB, FRED, RON AND JOEY!

I HATE SATURDAY NIGHTS.

RIGHT NOW? OH, NO, IRVING.. ..I REALLY DON'T WANT COMPANY THIS EVENING.

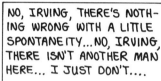

NO, IRVING, THERE'S NOTHING WRONG WITH A LITTLE SPONTANEITY...NO, IRVING, THERE ISN'T ANOTHER MAN HERE... I JUST DON'T....

IRVING, THIS IS NOT A REFLECTION OF MY FEELING TOWARDS OUR RELATIONSHIP ...BELIEVE ME... IRVING, PLEASE... I JUST DON'T WANT COMPANY RIGHT NOW.

ALL IN ALL, IT WOULD HAVE BEEN EASIER TO JUST TELL HIM MY HAIR WAS FILTHY.

THAT'S IT! I'M GOING TO STUFF THE REST OF THESE COOKIES DOWN THE GARBAGE DISPOSAL BEFORE I EAT THEM ALL.

JUST ONE MORE COOKIE, AND THEN THE REST OF THESE ARE GOING DOWN THE GARBAGE DISPOSAL!

OKAY, OKAY, I'LL JUST EAT UP THE BROKEN ONES, BUT THE REST ARE GOING DOWN THAT GARBAGE DISPOSAL!!

GOOD FOR YOU, CATHY. YOU GOT RID OF ALL THE COOKIES.

YOU WANT LOBSTER NEW-BURG, LINGUINI WITH CLAM SAUCE, TURKEY TETRAZZINI...

...CHICKEN PAPRIKASH, LASAGNA, BEEF BURGUNDY CREPES OR SPINACH SOUFFLÉ?

OH, IRVING, JUST A HAMBURGER WOULD BE FINE.

NAH, THAT'S TOO MUCH WORK.

IS THERE SOME GOOD REASON WHY YOU KEEP POPPING UP AND DOWN OUT OF YOUR CHAIR, CATHY?

YES, ANDREA.

POOL HOURS

I GET MY LEGS WET, THEN I LET THEM DRY IN THE HOT SUN... I GET THEM WET, I LET THEM DRY IN THE HOT SUN...

POOL HOURS

ISN'T IT A LITTLE LATE IN THE DAY TO BE WORRYING THAT MUCH ABOUT TANNING YOUR LEGS??

I'M NOT TANNING MY LEGS, ANDREA.

POOL HOURS

I'M TRYING TO SEE IF I CAN SHRINK THEM.

POOL HOURS

I'VE BEEN TRYING TO GET A MEETING GOING ALL DAY, CATHY. CAN YOU HELP ME GET EVERYONE IN THE SAME ROOM?

OF COURSE, MR. PINKLEY.

I'M GLAD YOU'VE COME TO RESPECT MY LEADERSHIP ABILITIES, AND I'M PROUD TO DEMONSTRATE THAT SPECIAL, MAGNETIC POWER A BUSINESS WOMAN HAS.

FREE DONUTS!!

PINKLEY

IT'S A LITTLE SOMETHING MY MOTHER TAUGHT ME.

NO, I CAN'T GO OUT, IRVING. I HAVE ANOTHER DATE.

WHY DIDN'T YOU JUST TELL HIM YOU'RE WORKING TONIGHT, CATHY?

I DIDN'T WANT TO GET INTO A BIG DISCUSSION ABOUT THE IMPORTANCE OF MY CAREER, ANDREA.

IRVING CAN UNDERSTAND ANOTHER MAN. IT'S A SITUATION HE CAN RELATE TO IN A DEEP, PERSONAL WAY.

TH

OH, IRVING, WAS THAT BEAUTIFUL SEE...

WHAT'S THAT, CATHY??

THAT WAS A STYROFOAM CUP. I SHREDDED IT TO PIECES WHILE I PLANNED MY STRATEGY FOR THE JACOBS PROJECT.

WHAT HAPPENED TO THIS??

THAT WAS MY CHAIR. I RIPPED OUT ALL THE LOOSE THREADS WHILE I THOUGHT UP MY OUTLINE.

I MUTILATED A BOX OF PAPER CLIPS, CHEWED UP 4 PENCILS, AND SCRIBBLED ALL OVER THE PHONE BOOK WHILE I WROTE MY FINAL DRAFT.

I CAN'T CREATE SOMETHING UNLESS I'M DESTROYING SOMETHING ELSE.

I WON'T BE IN TODAY, MR. PINKLEY. MY IRON IS THROWING UP.

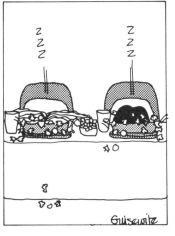

MR. PINKLEY, I CANNOT CONTINUE TO DO THE WORK OF 23 PEOPLE WHO ARE ON SUMMER VACATION.

I HAVE TAKEN IT UPON MYSELF TO HIRE A NEW TEMPORARY HELP SERVICE CALLED "M.O.M.".

IT STANDS FOR "MOTHERS ON THE MOVE" AND FRANKLY, MR. PINKLEY, I THINK THE 3 WOMEN THEY'RE SENDING OVER TODAY MAY JUST SAVE...

..MOM!

DON'T SHOUT, SWEETIE. ALL YOUR FILLINGS SHOW.

MOM, WHAT ARE YOU DOING IN MY OFFICE??

WE'RE THE TEMPORARY HELP SERVICE YOU HIRED... "MOTHERS ON THE MOVE".

IT'S OUR CONSCIOUSNESS-RAISING PROJECT FOR AUGUST. I TYPE, OLLIE FILES AND FLO BRINGS IN COFFEE CAKE.

OH, DON'T WORRY, CATHY. THIS IS STRICTLY BUSINESS. NOBODY WILL EVEN KNOW I'M YOUR MOTHER.

YOUNG LADY, YOUR ROOM IS A MESS!!

NO, CATHY ISN'T IN RIGHT NOW. MAY I TAKE A MESSAGE?

YEAH, THIS IS GREGORY.

TELL THAT SWEET THING THAT LAST NIGHT WAS ONLY THE BEGINNING.

WHEN I GET MY ARMS AROUND THAT CUTE LITTLE BODY TONIGHT, WHOOEE! WATCH OUT!!

ANY MESSAGES, MOM?

YES. YOU JUST BROKE UP WITH GREGORY.

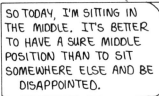

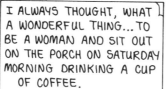

LOOK HOW SKINNY I WAS IN THIS OLD PICTURE, ANDREA. I THOUGHT I WAS SUCH A TUB THEN.

LOOK AT **THIS**. I THOUGHT I WAS SO FAT WHEN THIS WAS TAKEN... BUT I WAS A LITTLE TWIG.

OLD PICTURES CAN REALLY GIVE YOU A NEW PERSPECTIVE ON YOURSELF, CAN'T THEY, CATHY?

UH HUH...

BRING ON THE HOT FUDGE! I MUST BE THINNER THAN I THINK!

OH, CATHY, LOOK AT THIS...

FALL SALE $11.99

Fall Jackets now

CATHY?...

Fall Jackets now $29

CATHY??

Fall Skirts

FALL PANT SALE

HOW MANY TIMES HAVE I TOLD YOU NOT TO GO SHOPPING WHEN YOU'RE HUNGRY?

BLOUSES

EVERY DAY I HAVE LUNCH AT THE SAME PLACE AND EVERY DAY THE SAME MAN IS THERE EATING ALL BY HIMSELF, ANDREA.

YESTERDAY I THOUGHT... MAYBE HE KEEPS GOING THERE BECAUSE HE WANTS TO MEET **ME**... MAYBE HE'S TRYING TO WORK UP THE NERVE TO TALK TO **ME**!

ANDREA, MAYBE THIS MAN JUST LIVES FOR LUNCHTIME SO HE CAN CATCH A GLIMPSE OF **ME**!!

WANT ME TO GO WITH YOU TODAY AND CHECK HIM OUT?

NO... I DON'T WANT TO SCARE HIM OFF.

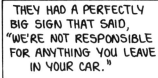

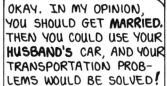

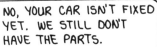
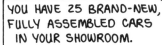

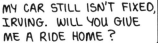

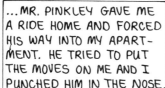

IRVING'S GOING TO RUSH THROUGH THAT DOOR WITH OPEN ARMS, AND HERE I AM, PLANNING AN ARGUMENT.

HE'S GOING TO SAY, "CATHY, MY DARLING!"...AND I'M GOING TO SAY, "IRVING, I'VE HAD IT!"

IRVING ALWAYS GETS ROMANTIC AND SWEET JUST WHEN I'M READY TO FIGHT.

CATHY, I'VE HAD IT!

IRVING, MY DARLING!

SOMETIMES I THINK IRVING TRIES TO BREAK UP WITH ME BEFORE THE HOLIDAYS JUST SO HE WON'T HAVE TO AGONIZE OVER WHAT TO GET ME.

THAT'S TERRIBLE, CATHY.

HOW COULD YOU POSSIBLY THINK IRVING WOULD STOOP THAT LOW??

SOMETIMES I THINK ABOUT DOING THE SAME THING.

HI. I'M LOOKING FOR A VERY NICE GIFT. DO YOU HAVE ANYTHING FOR AROUND $40?

OH, YES.

FOR $40 YOU CAN BUY THIS TINY POCKET COMPUTER WITH 37 SEPARATE GENIUS FUNCTIONS OPERATING OFF AN ELECTRIC BRAIN THE SIZE OF A PIN POINT...

OR, FOR $40, YOU CAN BUY THIS WASH'N'WEAR SHIRT.

DO YOU HAVE ANYTHING THAT DOESN'T FORCE ME TO MAKE THAT KIND OF CHOICE?

WHAT HAPPENED WHILE I WAS IN THE KITCHEN?

THE MAN WITH THE MISTY HAZEL EYES PASSED TO THE GUY WITH THE GORGEOUS LIPS.

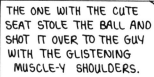

THE ONE WITH THE CUTE SEAT STOLE THE BALL AND SHOT IT OVER TO THE GUY WITH THE GLISTENING MUSCLE-Y SHOULDERS.

THEN THE GUY WITH THE FABULOUS JAW TOSSED BACK HIS AUBURN HAIR, AND PASSED TO THE GUY WITH THE GREAT LEGS WHO SMASHED THAT BABY IN FOR A SCORE!!

WHAT ARE YOU SO MAD FOR? I'M STARTING TO LIKE THIS SPORT.

Guisewite

CAN I HELP YOU?

YES. I NEED AN APPOINTMENT CALENDAR THAT WILL HELP ME STAY TOTALLY ORGANIZED.

HERE... WE HAVE "MONTH-AT-A-GLANCE", "WEEK-AT-A-GLANCE", OR "DAY-AT-A-GLANCE".

HOW MUCH OF YOUR BUSINESS SCHEDULE DID YOU WANT TO SEE AT A TIME?

DO YOU HAVE ANY "MINUTE-AT-A-GLANCE"?

Guisewite

SURE I'LL HELP WITH YOUR RESUME, CATHY... WHAT ARE YOUR MAIN ATTRIBUTES AS A BUSINESSWOMAN?

I'M ARTICULATE, CONSCIENTIOUS, DILIGENT AND ENTHUSIASTIC!

WHAT SPECIAL SKILLS DO YOU HAVE TO OFFER?

I'M ARTICULATE, CONSCIENTIOUS, DILIGENT AND ENTHUSIASTIC!

WHAT HAVE YOU ACHIEVED IN BUSINESS THUS FAR?

I'VE CONTINUED TO BE ARTICULATE, CONSCIENTIOUS, DILIGENT AND ENTHUSIASTIC!

LIFE ISN'T EASY FOR AN ENGLISH MAJOR.

Guisewite

WHY DID I TELL THAT GUY "NO"? I MIGHT HAVE HAD A GREAT TIME.

WHY WON'T I TAKE A CHANCE ON SOMEONE NEW? WHY CAN'T I LEARN TO RELAX AND SAY "YES"??

DING DONG!

HI. DO YOU WANT TO BUY...

YES! YES! YES! YES! YES!

NO DATE TONIGHT, CATHY?

NO. BUT I HAVE 400 NEW MAGAZINE SUBSCRIPTIONS.

I KNOW WHY WOMEN AREN'T PREPARED FOR LIFE, ANDREA. WE WASTED OUR GRADE SCHOOL EDUCATIONS WORRYING ABOUT OUR HAIR.

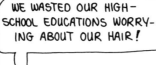

WE WASTED OUR HIGH-SCHOOL EDUCATIONS WORRYING ABOUT OUR HAIR!

WE WASTED OUR COLLEGE EDUCATIONS WORRYING ABOUT OUR HAIR!!

... ALL THINGS CONSIDERED, SHOULDN'T OUR HAIR LOOK BETTER THAN THIS?

WHEN I WAS YOUNG AND FRUSTRATED, I USED TO GO BUY A NEW RECORD.

WHEN I WAS OLDER AND FRUSTRATED, I USED TO GO BUY A NEW OUTFIT.

NOW I'M EVEN OLDER AND FRUSTRATED... AND SUDDENLY ALL I CAN THINK ABOUT IS BUYING A NEW COUCH.

THE OLDER I GET, THE MORE IT TAKES TO BUY ME OFF.

STEVE IS PICKING ME UP AT 8:00.

ANOTHER BLIND DATE?

YES. I CLEANED THE WHOLE HOUSE, HAD THE CURTAINS DRY CLEANED AND FIXED THE HOLE IN THE CARPETING.

AFTER DINNER, WE'RE COMING BACK HERE FOR DESSERT. I REFINISHED THE TABLE AND CHAIRS, REORGANIZED THE SHELVES, AND REWIRED THE COFFEE MAKER.

THIS HAS BEEN THE MOST PRODUCTIVE RELATIONSHIP OF MY LIFE AND WE HAVEN'T EVEN MET YET.

CATHY'S GOING TO GO BERSERK, BUT I HAVE TO GET HER EVALUATION OF LAST NIGHT'S DATE.

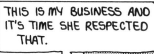

THIS IS MY BUSINESS AND IT'S TIME SHE RESPECTED THAT.

APARTMENTS 301-401

CATHY, I AM NOT MEDDLING. I JUST NEED TO KNOW...

MOM, YOU DID IT! STEVE WAS PERFECT! I LOVE YOU! I LOVE YOU!

MOTHERS ARE ALWAYS PREPARED FOR THE WRONG REACTION.

...AND THEN BRUCE SAID, "OOPS!" HA, HA... THEN BRUCE TOOK ME TO THE BALLET... BRUCE HAS THE CUTEST CAR... THEN BRUCE...

CHARLOTTE, ON BEHALF OF YOUR FAMILY, FRIENDS AND CO-WORKERS, I WOULD LIKE TO SAY WE'RE ALL GETTING A LITTLE BIT SICK OF HEARING ABOUT BRUCE.

CAN'T WE HAVE AN INTELLIGENT CONVERSATION BETWEEN TWO WOMEN WITHOUT DRAGGING BRUCE INTO IT EVERY 3 SECONDS?!

OKAY, OKAY. WHAT DO YOU WANT TO TALK ABOUT?

WELL, LAST NIGHT STEVE SAID THE CUTEST THING...

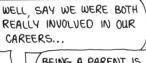

I HAVE 9 PROJECTS DUE BY FRIDAY, 47 LETTERS TO ANSWER AND 200 PHONE CALLS TO RETURN.

I'M 2 YEARS BEHIND ON MY FILING, I CAN'T FIND MY APPOINTMENT CALENDAR, AND MY SECRETARY'S THREATENING TO QUIT.

AND NOW MY BOYFRIEND, IRVING, WON'T TALK TO ME!

WHY WON'T IRVING TALK TO YOU?

HE'S THREATENED BY MY SUCCESS.

WHY ARE YOU GOING OUT WITH THAT EMERSON TWERP AGAIN, CATHY??

I LIKE HIM, IRVING. HE'S KIND OF VULNERABLE.

HEY, **I'M** KIND OF VULNERABLE.

HE'S SENSITIVE AND HUMAN, IRVING.

I'M SENSITIVE AND HUMAN!

HE ISN'T RUN BY HIS EGO, IRVING. HE JUST DOESN'T THINK HE'S PERFECT.

I'M LESS PERFECT THAN HE IS!!

THROUGHOUT HISTORY, WOMEN HAVE BEEN SUPPRESSED, REPRESSED AND OPPRESSED, IRVING.

WE'VE HAD MISERABLE JOBS, HIDEOUS PAY, HUMILIATING BENEFITS, AND NOT ONE SHRED OF RESPECT AS EQUAL HUMAN BEINGS.

WHAT POSSIBLE INJUSTICES DO YOU THINK MEN HAVE SUFFERED THAT EVEN COME **CLOSE**???

WE NEVER LEARNED TO CRY.

YOU NEVER HAD ANYTHING TO CRY ABOUT!!!

WHAT'S THE MATTER WITH YOU TWO, MOM?

FLO AND I ARE BUMMED OUT.

OUR DATING SERVICE FOLDED, AND NOW WE DON'T HAVE ANYTHING TO SAY WHEN OUR WOMEN FRIENDS ASK US WHAT WE DO.

WE HAVE TO MAKE WHOLE NEW DECISIONS ABOUT OUR LIVES.

I KNOW, MOM, I...

EITHER WE HAVE TO GO FIND NEW JOBS OR QUIT GOING TO COCKTAIL PARTIES.

YOU ARE NOT GOING TO TOUCH THAT GUACAMOLE DIP. YOU ARE NOT GOING TO EVEN **TASTE** THAT GUACAMOLE DIP!

OH YEAH?? HA, HA, HA!!

HI, CATHY. WHAT'S THE SCORE?

STOMACH, 400. BRAIN, 0.

YOUR BRIEFCASE IS FULL OF EMPTY COOKIE BOXES AND CANDY WRAPPERS, CATHY.

WHAT DID YOU BRING EMPTY COOKIE BOXES AND CANDY WRAPPERS HOME FOR??

DON'T YOU HAVE A WASTE-BASKET AT THE OFFICE??!

I DIDN'T WANT THE CLEANING PEOPLE TO KNOW I WAS CHEATING ON MY DIET.

THE REVENGE OF THE UNDERWEAR DRAWER.

I RESPECT YOU FOR WANTING TO MAKE A CAREER MOVE, ALICE, BUT I'M BEGGING YOU...PLEASE DON'T LEAVE.

YOUR SECRETARIAL WORK HAS MARKED THE DIFFERENCE BETWEEN SUCCESS AND FAILURE FOR ALL OF US. YOU'RE BRILLIANT AT WHAT YOU DO, AND A CRUCIAL LINK TO THE FUTURE OF THIS COMPANY !!

MR. PINKLEY, QUICK! WHAT ARE WE WILLING TO DO TO KEEP ALICE FROM QUITTING?!

HOW ABOUT A NEW TYPEWRITER COVER?

RUN FOR YOUR LIFE, ALICE.

ARE YOU FREE FOR A LUNCH MEETING, CATHY?

NO. TODAY IS ALICE'S GOING-AWAY PARTY. HOW ABOUT TOMORROW?

NO GOOD. TOMORROW IS JANET'S GOING-AWAY PARTY.

FRIDAY'S OUT. THAT'S BRIAN'S GOING-AWAY PARTY.

CATHY, YOU'RE NOT GOING TO QUIT, ARE YOU??

HOW COULD I QUIT NOW, MR. PINKLEY?

THERE'S NOBODY LEFT TO GO TO MY GOING-AWAY PARTY!!

SINGLE WOMEN ARE REALLY STARTING TO APPRECIATE BEING SINGLE, AND SUDDENLY ALL THE MEN ARE LOOKING FOR COMMITMENTS.

IT FIGURES. BUT WE'RE NOT GOING TO LET THAT STOP US, CATHY.

WE'VE FOUGHT FOR OUR FREEDOM AND **WE'RE GOING TO ENJOY IT** !!!

WHO ARE WE GOING TO GO OUT WITH ?

I HAVE TO GO TO A MEETING AND CHARLENE QUIT. YOU'RE IN CHARGE OF THE SWITCHBOARD, MR. PINKLEY.

ME ? DON'T BE RIDICULOUS, CATHY.

THAT SWITCHBOARD IS A HIGHLY COMPLEX COMPUTER ... AN ELECTRONIC BRAIN CAPABLE OF RECEIVING AND DIRECTING HUNDREDS OF CALLS SIMULTANEOUSLY.

THAT'S WOMAN'S WORK !

I DON'T THINK I SAW YOUR BEDROOM WHEN YOU GAVE ME THE TOUR...

MY BEDROOM, JOHN ?

YES, YOUR **BEDROOM**, CATHY ! WHERE **IS** THAT BEDROOM ??!

NEVER MIND.

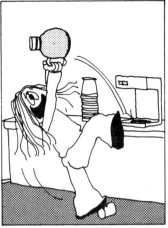

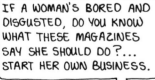

CAN I HELP YOU?

YES. YOU HAVE 277 BATHING SUITS ON YOUR RACK AND OF THOSE, 276 ARE THE NEW HIGH-CUT LEG LOOK.

THERE ARE 115,000,000 WOMEN IN THIS COUNTRY. OF THOSE, APPROXIMATELY 3 WOULD LOOK GOOD IN A SUIT LIKE THIS.

I WANT TO KNOW **WHY**. WHY WOULD YOU STOCK AN ENTIRE DEPARTMENT FULL OF WOMEN'S SUITS THAT ONLY **3 WOMEN** IN THE ENTIRE COUNTRY COULD WEAR??!!

WHAT'S WRONG WITH THESE SUITS? I'VE BEEN VERY HAPPY WITH MINE.

HM! ONE OF THE LUCKY ONES!

IRVING, IF YOU COULD JUST LEARN TO TALK ABOUT WHAT YOU THINK ABOUT, IT COULD DO WONDERS FOR OUR RELATIONSHIP.

OKAY, CATHY. I'LL TALK.

...YESTERDAY I WAS COMING DOWN THE ELEVATOR WHEN THIS GORGEOUS BLOND STARTS STARING AT ME. WELL, I FELT A LITTLE INSECURE...

... I MEAN, I COULD HAVE BEEN WRONG, BUT THIS LADY WAS DEFINITELY LOOKING INTERESTED. WHAT THE HECK, I FIGURED,... BETTER CHECK THIS BABY OUT! WELL, NEXT THING YOU KNOW, WE'RE...

I FAIL TO SEE HOW THIS IS BRINGING US ANY CLOSER, CATHY.

HI, CATHY. WANT TO HAVE DINNER?

NO, IRVING. I'M NOT SEEING YOU AGAIN UNTIL YOU CHANGE YOUR WAYS.

..HEY, SHARON! HOW ABOUT COMING OVER AND WHIPPING UP SOME OF YOUR FAMOUS BEEF STROGANOFF??

FORGET IT, IRVING.

..HELLO, MARILYN! WHAT'S A GORGEOUS THING LIKE YOU DOING HOME ON A SATURDAY NIGHT??

BUZZ OFF, IRVING.

...HI, CATHY. I'VE CHANGED.

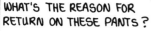

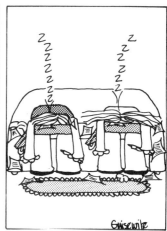

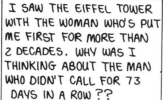

BONJOUR, MR. BIALKO!

MOM, DON'T ENCOURAGE HIM.

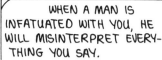

WHEN A MAN IS INFATUATED WITH YOU, HE WILL MISINTERPRET EVERYTHING YOU SAY.

A DESPERATE MAN WILL TAKE EVERY LITTLE WORD, EVERY DECENT GESTURE AS A SIGN OF ENCOURAGEMENT.

FINIS?

OUR WAITER IS IN LOVE WITH ME.

MOM, AM I HALLUCINATING, OR DID YOU JUST PUT ON YOUR BRAND-NEW HAT FOR THAT NICE MR. BIALKO?

AM I DREAMING, OR ARE YOU WEARING YOUR BRAND-NEW HAT BECAUSE YOU'RE A LITTLE BIT FLATTERED BY THAT NICE MR. BIALKO'S ATTENTIONS?

AM I MAKING THIS UP, OR ARE YOU ABOUT TO GO MARCHING AROUND PARIS IN YOUR BRAND-NEW HAT WITH THAT NICE MR. BIALKO WHILE YOUR HUSBAND, MY FATHER, IS ALL ALONE AT HOME WITH A TV DINNER?

AM I IMAGINING THINGS, OR ARE YOU STARTING TO SOUND LIKE YOUR MOTHER?

YAACK! THAT NICE MR. BIALKO THINKS WE'RE HAVING A "LITTLE FLING"!!

I TRIED TO TELL YOU THIS WAS HAPPENING, MOM.

WHAT AM I GOING TO DO, CATHY?? I'LL HAVE TO HIDE IN MY ROOM!

OH NO YOU WON'T.

WE ARE NOT GOING TO WASTE OUR PRECIOUS TIME HIDING FROM A MAN WHO HAS A CRUSH ON YOU. THIS IS OUR VACATION IN PARIS!

WE'RE SUPPOSED TO BE WASTING OUR PRECIOUS TIME HIDING FROM A MAN WHO HAS A CRUSH ON ME.

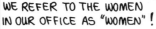

THERE'S NO ANSWER. HOW CAN THERE BE NO ANSWER? HE HAS AN ANSWERING MACHINE.

RING RING RING RING

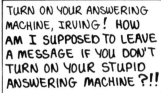

TURN ON YOUR ANSWERING MACHINE, IRVING! HOW AM I SUPPOSED TO LEAVE A MESSAGE IF YOU DON'T TURN ON YOUR STUPID ANSWERING MACHINE?!!

RING RING RING RING

WHAT'S WRONG WITH **YOU**, CATHY?

I'M MAD BECAUSE I DIDN'T GET A RECORDING.

ARE YOU DATING ANYONE, CATHY?

WELL, I'VE BEEN SEEING THIS GUY NAMED IRVING, BUT WE STILL GO OUT WITH OTHER PEOPLE.

I GO OUT WITH A WOMAN NAMED SUSAN, BUT IT ISN'T SERIOUS.

I OCCASIONALLY DATE EMERSON, BUT THERE REALLY ISN'T A FUTURE THERE.

I'VE BEEN SEEING PAULA... ...NAH, PAULA MEANS NOTHING TO ME.

ARE YOU READY TO LEAVE YET, CATHY?

NOT QUITE. DONALD AND I ARE STILL REVIEWING OUR PRIOR LACK-OF-COMMITMENTS.

HI, MOM. HOW WAS YOUR MEETING?

TERRIBLE. THOSE WOMEN HAVE NO SENSE OF PURPOSE.

MY ENTIRE CONSCIOUSNESS-RAISING SESSION DETERIORATED INTO A CHEAP FIGHT OVER WHOSE DAUGHTER SHOULD BE MARRYING PRINCE CHARLES.

OH, MOM... I'M SORRY.

HE NEVER EVEN GOT TO **MEET** YOU!!

RING
RING
RING

DID YOU LET IRVING HAVE IT FOR NOT SHOWING UP LAST NIGHT, CATHY?

I WAS FURIOUS LAST NIGHT, ANDREA.

BUT THEN I STARTED THINKING... WAS WHAT HE DID ACTUALLY ANY WORSE THAN SOME OF THE THINGS I'VE DONE?

I'VE BEEN THOUGHTLESS AND INCONSIDERATE... I'VE GOTTEN MYSELF INTO MESSES... I'VE HURT SOME FINE PEOPLE, ANDREA... I'VE DONE HORRIBLE THINGS!!

WHAT DID YOU SAY TO IRVING?

SOMEHOW I WOUND UP BEGGING HIM TO FORGIVE ME.

I DON'T SEEM TO HAVE ANY MONEY IN HERE. WILL YOU TAKE A CHECK?

OH, I DON'T SEEM TO HAVE A PEN. MAY I BORROW... ...NEVER MIND.. I DON'T SEEM TO HAVE MY CHECK-BOOK WITH ME.

WILL YOU TAKE A CHARGE CARD? AHEM... WAIT... I DON'T SEEM TO HAVE MY CHARGE CARDS WITH ME, EITHER.

HOW EMBARRASSING. I'VE BEEN CARRYING AROUND 300 GUM WRAPPERS FOR THE LAST FOUR DAYS.

MEN INVEST THEIR MONEY IN THE STOCK MARKET AND WOMEN SPEND THEIR MONEY ON MAKE-UP SO WE CAN LURE THEM.

NOTHING'S CHANGED, ANDREA. IRVING'S OUT THERE BUILDING A FINANCIAL FUTURE FOR HIMSELF AND WHAT DO I HAVE? "GLIMMERY ROSE-BUD" CHEEKS!

CATHY, THERE IS ONE REASON AND ONE REASON ALONE WHY A MAN LIKE IRVING IS INVESTING HIS MONEY MORE PRODUCTIVELY THAN YOU!

HE HAS $5000.00 AND I HAVE 89¢.

"DEAR MIDLAND HIGH SCHOOL GRADUATE, PLEASE JOIN US AT OUR CLASS REUNION, AUGUST 28, 1981."

"THIS IS YOUR CHANCE TO HAVE 600 EX-CLASSMATES STARE AT YOU AND SEE WHETHER YOU GOT FAT AND/OR WOUND UP WITH A LOSER"..."

"IN ONE FUN-FILLED EVENING, WE WILL RE-CREATE EVERY INSECURITY YOU'VE SPENT THE LAST 10 YEARS TRYING TO OVERCOME. SEE YOU THERE! (OR ELSE WE'LL REALLY TALK!)..."

NICE TO SEE THEY HAVEN'T LOST THE OLD SCHOOL SPIRIT.

AT 5:32 I GOT AN INVITATION TO MY HIGH SCHOOL REUNION. AT 5:55 CONNIE KRAMER CALLED LONG DISTANCE AND BEGGED ME TO BE ON THE DECORATING COMMITTEE.

HOW DID THEY FIND YOU SO FAST? YOU DON'T LIVE IN THE SAME TOWN ANYMORE.

YOU DIDN'T STAY IN TOUCH WITH ANYONE FROM HIGH SCHOOL. HOW DID THEY EVEN KNOW WHERE YOU WERE?

PEOPLE NEVER LOSE TRACK OF WOMEN WHO KNOW HOW TO MAKE TISSUE PAPER FLOWERS.

LOOK AT ME IN MY HIGH SCHOOL YEARBOOK, ANDREA. WHAT A LOSER.

PEOPLE WHO FELT LIKE REJECTS IN HIGH SCHOOL OFTEN GO ON TO DO GREAT THINGS, CATHY.

INSECURE PEOPLE ARE DRIVEN TO ACCOMPLISH MUCH MORE THAN PEOPLE WHO HAVE FELT COOL ALL THEIR LIVES.

IT'S ALMOST LIKE THE WORSE YOU FELT ABOUT YOURSELF IN HIGH SCHOOL THE BETTER YOU'LL DO AS AN ADULT!

JUST MY LUCK. I WASN'T A BIG ENOUGH LOSER.

THIS WAS MY BEST FRIEND IN HIGH SCHOOL. SHE GOT MARRIED. HERE'S MY OTHER BEST FRIEND. MARRIED.

THIS ONE GOT MARRIED, DI-VORCED AND RE-MARRIED. THIS ONE'S MARRIED. LET'S SEE... MARRIED... MARRIED ...MARRIED... DIVORCED... MARRIED...MARRIED.

CATHY, THIS DOESN'T MAKE YOU FEEL BAD, DOES IT?

NO.. IT JUST MAKES ME REALIZE HOW DIFFERENT MY LIFE IS.

I'M GOING TO BE THE ONLY ONE AT MY HIGH SCHOOL REUNION WHO DOESN'T HAVE A FONDUE SET.

THERE WERE TWO KINDS OF GIRLS IN HIGH SCHOOL... THE ONES WHO DANCED AND GOT CRAZY, AND THE ONES WHO RAN AROUND STICKING THE FLOWERS BACK ON THE FLOATS.

THAT WAS ME, ANDREA. CONSCIENTIOUS AND DATE-LESS. HO, HO! WAIT'LL MY GRADUATING CLASS SEES ME NOW!! HO, HO!!!

PEOPLE LIKE IT WHEN YOU'RE CONSISTENT.

YOU FOUND OUT ABOUT YOUR HIGH SCHOOL REUNION LAST WEDNESDAY, CATHY. WHY DIDN'T YOU START YOUR DIET THEN?

IT'S BAD LUCK TO START A DIET ON WEDNESDAY, ANDREA.

NOBODY EVER LOST WEIGHT ON A DIET THAT STARTED ON THURSDAY OR FRIDAY... ...SATURDAY AND SUNDAY ARE OUT BECAUSE THEY'RE THE WEEKEND. MONDAY? TOO PREDICTABLE.

THE ONLY DIET THAT HAS A CHANCE OF MAKING IT IS A DIET THAT STARTS **BRIGHT AND EARLY TUESDAY MORNING!**

...EACH OF US HAS HER OWN LITTLE SYSTEM FOR FAILURE.

I THOUGHT I MIGHT WEAR THIS DRESS TO MY HIGH SCHOOL REUNION, MOM.

OH, YOU LOOK ADORABLE IN THAT DRESS, CATHY!

THEN AGAIN, I THOUGHT I MIGHT WEAR THIS OUTFIT.

OH, YOU LOOK JUST GORGEOUS IN THAT OUTFIT!

THEN AGAIN, I THOUGHT I MIGHT RIP DOWN MY LIVING ROOM CURTAINS, THROW THEM OVER MY HEAD AND STAPLE ALUMINUM FOIL ALL OVER MYSELF.

OH, SWEETIE, YOU'D BE THE MOST BEAUTIFUL ONE THERE!!

I LOVE MY MOTHER.

HEY, CATHY. IS THAT YOU? IT'S ME. REMEMBER ME?

MHS

* WELCOME *
MIDLAND HIGH SCHOOL
CLASS REUNION

CATHY! HOW ARE YOU DOING??

CATHY, CATHY, CATHY! LONG TIME, NO SEE!

MHS

I THOUGHT EVERYONE WAS SUPPOSED TO BE OLD AND FAT!!!

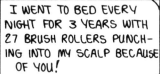

THIS WOMAN NEVER SPOKE TO ME THE ENTIRE TIME WE WERE IN HIGH SCHOOL. SHE WAS TOO COOL.

"YAK YAK YAK YAK"

NOW SHE RAN OVER TO ME AND IS YAKKING AWAY LIKE SHE WAS MY BEST FRIEND.

"YAK YAK YAK"

"YAK YAK YAK YAK YAK YAK"

CELLULITE. THE GREAT EQUALIZER.

"YAK YAK YAK YAK"

OF COURSE, YOU KNEW WHAT A CRUSH I HAD ON YOU IN HIGH SCHOOL, CATHY...

YOU HAD A CRUSH ON ME IN HIGH SCHOOL?

EVERYONE IN THE WHOLE SCHOOL KNEW I HAD A CRUSH ON YOU.

I DIDN'T KNOW YOU HAD A CRUSH ON ME.

HOW COULD YOU NOT KNOW I HAD A CRUSH ON YOU?? THE ENTIRE WORLD KNEW I HAD A CRUSH ON YOU!!!

DO YOU STILL??

OH, CATHY! YOU'RE BACK FROM YOUR REUNION! TELL ME ALL ABOUT IT!

I SURVIVED, MOM.

I HAVE LOOKED MY PAST IN THE EYE, AND I'VE COME AWAY INTACT.

I LEFT THERE TOTALLY CONTENT WITH MY LIFE. I'M SATISFIED WITH MY ACCOMPLISHMENTS, AND I'M PROUD OF MYSELF AS A WOMAN AND A HUMAN BEING!!

COME ON, CATHY... ...GET TO THE GOOD STUFF.

I HAD MY EYE ON HIM THE WHOLE SEMINAR, BUT I NEVER TALKED TO HIM, ANDREA.

AND THEN JUST WHEN EVERYONE WAS LEAVING, I SAID, "WAIT A MINUTE, CATHY. ARE YOU GOING TO LET THIS MOMENT SLIP BETWEEN YOUR FINGERS LIKE ALL THOSE OTHERS??"

"ARE YOU GOING TO LET THIS MAN WHO FASCINATES YOU WALK OUT OF YOUR LIFE FOREVER BECAUSE YOU COULDN'T UTTER ONE MEASLY HELLO?? NO!" I SAID, "NO, NO, NO!!!"

ALL **RIGHT**! WHAT DID YOU SAY TO HIM??

NOTHING. BY THE TIME I FINISHED GIVING MYSELF THE LECTURE, HE'D ALREADY LEFT.

HELLO, DAVID? DAVID, THIS IS CATHY FROM OHIO. I SAW YOU AT THE MANAGEMENT SEMINAR, I WAS FASCINATED, I CAN'T GET YOU OUT OF MY MIND, AND I WANT TO KNOW YOU BETTER.

CATHY, I CAN'T BELIEVE YOU CALLED. I'VE THOUGHT ABOUT YOU EVERY MOMENT SINCE THAT DAY!! I DIDN'T KNOW WHERE YOU LIVED... I COULDN'T REMEMBER HOW TO SPELL YOUR LAST NAME...

I'VE BEEN FRANTICALLY CALLING EVERYONE I KNOW WHO MIGHT KNOW HOW TO REACH YOU.

OH, HEE HEE HEE HEE HEE HEE HEE HEE

WHY CAN'T THE NEW ME EVER LAST FOR MORE THAN 3 SENTENCES?

ARE YOU STILL THERE, CATHY?

YES, I'M STILL HERE. ...GOODNIGHT AGAIN, DAVID.

GOODNIGHT...THIS IS SILLY. I CAN'T SEEM TO HANG UP.

I KNOW, BUT WE HAVE TO. IT'S LONG DISTANCE AND IT'S COSTING A FORTUNE. GOODNIGHT.

GOODNIGHT... ARE YOU STILL THERE?

YES...BUT NOW THIS IS REALLY IT. WE HAVE TO SAY GOODNIGHT...

OKAY...GOODNIGHT *CLICK!*

I WAS JUST GETTING WARMED UP.

MAYBE DAVID LOST MY PHONE NUMBER, ANDREA...

MEN DON'T LOSE WOMEN'S PHONE NUMBERS, CATHY.

THEY THROW THEM ALL ONTO LITTLE TRAYS ON TOP OF THEIR DRESSERS. THEN WHEN MEN GET BORED, THEY FISH THROUGH THE TRAY AND PULL OUT A LUCKY WINNER AND THAT'S WHO THEY CALL.

THAT'S WHO THEY CALL, WHO THEY DATE, WHO THEY MARRY, WHO THEY GET PREGNANT, WHO THEY DIVORCE, AND WHO THEY DON'T PAY ANY ALIMONY TO!!

HI, CATHY. IT'S DAVID.

WHAT DO **YOU** WANT?!!

WHERE IS EVERYONE? WE'RE SUPPOSED TO HAVE A MEETING AT 8:30.

MR. PINKLEY, PLEASE COME IN HERE. LEE, WILL YOU AND BETTY QUIT WAITING FOR EVERYONE ELSE TO COME TO THE MEETING BEFORE YOU DO??

NO, ALAN, YOU MAY **NOT** RUN OUT TO WARM UP YOUR COFFEE! NO ONE IS LEAVING THIS ROOM UNTIL... GET BACK IN HERE, JOHN!

TIRED?

I'M EXHAUSTED. I SPENT THE WHOLE MORNING ALMOST IN A MEETING.

I HAVEN'T LEFT THE APARTMENT FOR 6 HOURS BECAUSE DAVID SAID HE'D CALL AND I KNOW THAT SOMETIMES HIS BUSINESS GETS IN THE WAY, JUST LIKE MINE DOES.

I'M WAITING FOR HIM TO CALL INSTEAD OF ME CALLING HIM BECAUSE I KNOW WHAT I HAVE TO OFFER, AND HE'D BE A FOOL IF HE DIDN'T RECOGNIZE IT.

NOW I'M EATING A ONE-POUND BAG OF M&M'S BECAUSE I NO LONGER FEEL I HAVE TO BE A SIZE 3 TO BE A VIABLE, ATTRACTIVE MEMBER OF SOCIETY.

I'M DOING ALL THE WRONG THINGS FOR ALL THE RIGHT REASONS.

THAT WAS KAREN. HER BOY-FRIEND DUMPED HER, SHE GOT MAD, STARTED HER OWN BUSINESS AND JUST GROSSED $500,000.00 IN SALES.

JOAN WENT TO HAWAII TO RECOVER FROM BEING FIRED, LANDED A REAL ESTATE DEAL, AND IS MANAGING HER OWN STRING OF CONDO-MINIUMS ON THE BEACH.

PAULA GOT FAT, FOUNDED A WEIGHT LOSS CLINIC, LOST 53 POUNDS, AND FELL IN LOVE WITH THE MOST HAND-SOME MAN I'VE EVER SEEN IN MY LIFE.

EVERYONE I KNOW IS HAVING A MORE PRODUCTIVE CRISIS THAN I AM.

WHAT A GREAT MOVIE! I LOVED THAT MOVIE, IRVING.

YEAH, ME TOO.

OH, IRVING...PLEASE DON'T JUMP IN THE CAR AND TURN THE RADIO ON LIKE YOU USUALLY DO, OKAY?

HUH?

I WANT THIS MOVIE TO LAST IN MY HEAD AND WHEN YOU TURN THE RADIO ON IT BREAKS THE WHOLE SPELL.

WE'RE NOT EVEN IN THE **PARKING** LOT YET! MAYBE I WASN'T **GOING** TO TURN THE RADIO ON!!

TURN THE RADIO ON, IRVING.

MOVIE PARKING

SHOULD I TELL IRVING ABOUT DAVID OR NOT, ANDREA? I DON'T KNOW WHAT TO DO.

I GUESS I SHOULD TELL HIM. NO. THAT WOULD BE STUPID. I'LL WAIT AND SEE WHAT HAPPENS. THEN I'LL TELL HIM.

NO. I'LL TELL HIM RIGHT NOW. NO. I DON'T KNOW. SHOULD I TELL HIM OR SHOULDN'T I TELL HIM??

COOKIES

WHAT DOES THE LITTLE VOICE INSIDE YOU SAY?

EAT EAT EAT EAT

COOKIES

OF **COURSE** YOUR MOTHER WOULD BE UPSET IF YOU TOLD HER YOU WERE RUNNING OFF TO SPEND A WEEKEND IN ST. LOUIS WITH A MAN YOU BARELY KNOW.

WHY DO YOU NEED TO TELL HER? I KNOW WHY... **APPROVAL.** IF **SHE** KNOWS, YOU CAN SOMEHOW PUT THE WHOLE BURDEN FOR WHATEVER HAPPENS ON HER.

YOU'RE NOT TELLING YOUR MOTHER TO BE HONEST, CATHY... YOU'RE TELLING HER SO **YOU WON'T FEEL SO GUILTY!!**

SOUNDS GOOD TO ME.

WHAT ARE YOU TAKING TO ST. LOUIS?

WELL, DAVID SAID WE MIGHT PLAY A LITTLE TENNIS.

THEN I THOUGHT WE'D HAVE A ROMANTIC PICNIC IN THE PARK, SEE A BEAUTIFUL, SENSITIVE COMEDY, HAVE DINNER IN A CHARMING FRENCH RESTAURANT, LAUGH, TALK...

...DANCE UNDER THE STARS, AND FALL SO TOTALLY IN LOVE WITH EACH OTHER THAT DAVID WOULD BEG ME TO STAY FOR FOUR MONTHS.

HOPE FILLS UP A LOT OF SUITCASES.

EXCUSE ME... I'M VERY SORRY... THIS IS THE LAST TIME I'LL BOTHER YOU.

YOU MUST BE GOING TO SEE SOMEONE VERY SPECIAL.

WELL, YES. YES I AM! I GUESS IT SHOWS.

YES, IT SHOWS.

PLUS THE FACT THAT EVERY TIME YOU COME BACK FROM THE LADIES ROOM YOUR COLOGNE IS A LITTLE BIT STRONGER AND NOW I CAN HARDLY BREATHE.

EXCUSE ME... I BEG YOUR PARDON...

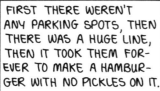

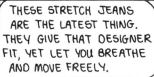

DAVID! WHAT ARE **YOU** DOING IN TOWN?? I...

HELLO, BEAUTIFUL... AND YOU MUST BE IRVING. I'VE HEARD SO MUCH ABOUT YOU.

I HAVE ONLY THE GREATEST RESPECT FOR YOUR RELATIONSHIP WITH CATHY, IRVING... ...BUT I FIND MYSELF IN THE AWKWARD POSITION OF WANTING TO SPEND TIME WITH HER, TOO.

I HOPED THAT IF WE COULD TALK THIS OVER IN PERSON, IT MIGHT MAKE THINGS LESS UNCOMFORTABLE FOR EVERYONE. CAN I BUY YOU A DRINK, IRVING?

WHAT THE HECK?

HOW DID YOU FEEL WHEN I CAME OVER TO CATHY'S AND TOLD YOU HOW MUCH I WANTED TO GO OUT WITH HER?

I FELT LIKE PUNCHING YOUR FACE IN.

YEAH, WELL... I GUESS WE'VE ALL BEEN THERE. BY SMASHING SOMEONE'S FACE YOU RELIEVE THE TENSION WITHOUT HAVING TO ADMIT THAT YOU FEEL HURT.

IT'S JUST CONDITIONING, IRVING. WE ALL BOUGHT IT. THEY TAUGHT US IT WAS MORE MANLY TO ACT LIKE 6-YEAR-OLDS THAN TO TALK ABOUT HOW WE FEEL.

NOW I REALLY FEEL LIKE PUNCHING YOUR FACE IN.

I'VE COME TO SHOW YOU ST. LOUIS IN THE FALL! OUR PLANE LEAVES IN AN HOUR.

AN **HOUR**? DAVID, WHAT ABOUT WORK? WHAT ABOUT IRVING??

CATHY, IF WE WAIT FOR EVERYTHING TO BE CONVENIENT, WE'RE GOING TO MISS ANY CHANCE WE EVER HAD.

YOU CAN DO THIS... JUST ONCE, STOP YOUR LIFE IN ITS TRACKS, LOOK THE WORLD IN THE EYE AND SAY, "**I'M** IN CHARGE! THE NEXT THREE DAYS BELONG TO **ME**!!"

EVERY TIME I TAKE CHARGE OF MY OWN LIFE SOMEBODY ELSE IS HOLDING THE TICKET.

I APOLOGIZE FOR THE LACK OF WARNING, MR. PINKLEY, BUT I MUST TAKE A FEW PERSONAL DAYS OFF STARTING TODAY.

CHARLENE IS COVERING ON THE KLINE PROJECT. ALAN IS TAKING CARE OF THE RILEY ACCOUNT. AND I ASKED JILL TO LOOK OVER THE BRADLEY FIGURES...AM I FORGETTING ANYTHING?

THE HOSTESS HO-HO'S ARE IN MY BOTTOM RIGHT HAND DRAWER.

MMMM...

I HAVEN'T HAD ONE OF THESE IN YEARS!

HERE, TRY THIS ONE, DAVID!

OOH... MY FAVORITE!

♪ TRICK OR TREAT ♪

YAAAA!

CATHY, WHEN YOU SAY "I DON'T KNOW WHAT I WANT FOR LUNCH" WHAT YOU'RE REALLY THINKING IS "I DON'T KNOW WHAT **YOU** WANT FOR LUNCH."

YOU'LL NEVER MAKE DECISIONS IN OUR RELATIONSHIP IF YOU TRY TO SECOND GUESS **ME** ALL THE TIME.

I WANT YOU TO BE AN EQUAL VOICE IN EVERYTHING WE DO. DON'T **THINK** ABOUT ME... JUST **SAY** WHAT **YOU** WANT FOR LUNCH!!

GIVE ME A HINT.

INTRODUCING A REMARKABLE NEW SCENT FOR THE REMARKABLE NEW YOU.

STRONG AND SASSY, YET FEMININE AND FLIRTATIOUS... ...SELF-CONFIDENT YET CUDDLY... DEMANDING YET DEMURE...

DECISIVE... QUESTIONING... DEFIANT... DREAMY... BOLD... BLUSHING... IT'S HERE. IT'S NEW. IT'S ALL THE WOMEN YOU ARE, IN ONE LITTLE BOTTLE.

I DON'T THINK I WANT TO SMELL THAT CONFUSED.

DAVID SPENT 2 HOURS ON THE PHONE LAST NIGHT TELLING ME HE LOVES ME.

HE SAID, "CATHY, I LOVE YOU TODAY AND I WILL LOVE YOU FOREVER!!"

WELL, I GUESS THIS LEAVES ONLY ONE QUESTION.

I KNOW.

WILL HE STILL LOVE ME AFTER HE GETS HIS PHONE BILL?

I WATCHED THE MORNING NEWS, THE NOON NEWS, THE EVENING NEWS AND THE LATE-NIGHT NEWS.

I SAW THE LOCAL NEWS, THE NATIONAL NEWS, AND THE WORLD NEWS.

I WATCHED "NEWS BRIEF", "NEWS BREAK", "NEWS UPDATE", "NEWS CLOSE-UP", "NEWS WRAP-UP", "NEWS HIGHLIGHTS", "NEWS ANALYSIS" AND "NEWS REVIEW".

WHY DON'T I KNOW WHAT'S GOING ON?!

I LOVE THE FALL.

IT'S HARD WHEN YOU'RE THE ONE WHO ENDS A RELATIONSHIP, CATHY...YOU QUIT THINKING ABOUT THE MAN AS THE ONE YOU DUMPED AND START THINKING ABOUT HIM AS **A MAN WHO GOT DUMPED ON.**

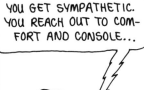
YOU GET SYMPATHETIC. YOU REACH OUT TO COMFORT AND CONSOLE...

...AND SUDDENLY, YOU'RE BACK ON THE COUCH TELLING JOKES AND EATING DORRITOS WITH THE GUY YOU WERE NEVER GOING TO SPEAK TO AGAIN.

ANDREA HAS THE LIVING ROOM BUGGED.

YOU WENT OUT AND GOT DRUNK BECAUSE YOU WERE JEALOUS? THAT WAS STUPID.

HOW IS THAT ANY MORE STUPID THAN YOU **EATING** WHEN YOU'RE JEALOUS?

IRVING, I EAT WHEN I'M **DEPRESSED.** I BUY **SHOES** WHEN I'M JEALOUS. I BREAK THE TELEPHONE WHEN I'M ANGRY...

I MANGLE MY FINGERNAILS WHEN I'M LONELY...I THROW THINGS ALL OVER THE HOUSE WHEN I'M HURT...AND I WASTE MONEY ON MAKE-UP WHEN I'M FRUSTRATED.

MEN JUST DON'T KNOW HOW TO COPE.

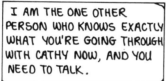

DAVID WAS FEELING HOSTILE AND DEFENSIVE BECAUSE OF IRVING... SO I SAID, "DAVID, HONEY, I'LL MAKE IT UP TO YOU. COME TO THANKS-GIVING DINNER AT MY MOM'S."

MEANWHILE, IRVING WASN'T SPEAKING TO ME BECAUSE OF DAVID. I SAID "IRVING, DARLING, I'LL MAKE IT UP TO YOU. COME TO THANKS-GIVING DINNER AT MY MOM'S."

ANDREA, I DIDN'T MEAN TO, BUT I WOUND UP INVITING BOTH OF THEM TO THANKSGIVING DINNER AT MY MOM'S!!

HOW COULD I DO THIS?? EVERYTHING WAS GOING SO WELL!

HOW COULD I INVITE BOTH DAVID AND IRVING FOR THANKSGIVING, MOM?! THIS IS THE DUMBEST THING I'VE EVER DONE IN MY LIFE!

OH, SWEETIE...

REMEMBER WHEN YOU HAD 3 DATES FOR THAT DANCE IN HIGH SCHOOL? THAT WAS MUCH DUMBER THAN THIS. HOW ABOUT THE TIME YOU WROTE THAT HUMILIATING LETTER AND TRIED TO STEAL IT BACK?? VERY DUMB.

OH, AND REMEMBER WHEN YOU CALLED ME FROM THE LADIES ROOM OF THAT RES-TAURANT AND HAD ME RUSH OVER AND FIX YOUR ZIPPER SO YOUR DINNER DATE WOULDN'T KNOW?? HOO BOY! THERE HAVE BEEN SOME LU-LU'S!!

THANKS.

WHAT'S A MOTHER FOR?

OH, WHAT A THANKSGIVING! MY HUSBAND...MY BEAUTI-FUL DAUGHTER...AND HER TWO HANDSOME DATES!!

IRVING, YOU LOOK SO CUTE IN YOUR NECKTIE!

DAVID, YOU'RE JUST ADORABLE!

WELL, I GUESS I DON'T HAVE TO SAY WHAT ONE BIG QUESTION IS ON ALL OF OUR MINDS TODAY!!!

ARE YOU GOING TO BE LIKE YOUR MOTHER WHEN YOU'RE HER AGE?

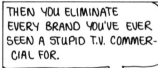

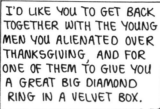

MR. PINKLEY? JOANNE? OKAY... I THINK WE'RE FINALLY ALL HERE.

WE HAVE MANY IMPORTANT THINGS ON OUR AGENDA TODAY, SO LET'S NOT WASTE ANY MORE TIME.

ALL THOSE IN FAVOR OF **NOT** HOLDING OUR OFFICE CHRISTMAS PARTY ON A WEEK NIGHT NEXT YEAR, SAY "AYE".

THESE CHRISTMAS CARDS ARE FOR MY BUSINESS FRIENDS WHO CHANGED JOBS AND I CAN'T REMEMBER WHERE THEY WORK NOW.

THESE ARE FOR MY PERSONAL FRIENDS WHO MOVED LAST YEAR AND I CAN'T FIND THEIR NEW ADDRESSES.

THESE ARE FOR MY FRIENDS WHO EITHER GOT MARRIED OR DIVORCED AND NOBODY KNOWS WHAT NAME THEY'RE GOING BY ANYMORE.

I NEVER REALIZED HOW STABLE I WAS BEFORE.

THAT SIMPLE DRESS CAN BECOME AN ENTIRE WARDROBE OF GREAT HOLIDAY LOOKS.

THIS?

SEE? YOU CAN BELT IT, BLOUSE IT, WRAP IT, LAYER IT, TUNIC IT, SASH IT, TUCK IT...

THE VARIETIES ARE ENDLESS! HARD TO BELIEVE, ISN'T IT?!!

YES. WITH JUST ONE DRESS, I HAVE LOOKED TERRIBLE IN 23 DIFFERENT OUTFITS.

HOW ABOUT SOME KITCHEN-WARE FOR YOUR DAUGHTER?

OH, NO. CATHY WILL THINK I'M MAKING AN ISSUE OF THE FACT THAT SHE ISN'T MARRIED YET AND SHOULD ALREADY HAVE ALL THAT STUFF.

HOW ABOUT SOMETHING FOR HER OFFICE?

NO. SHE'LL THINK I'M PURPOSELY AVOIDING ANYTHING TO DO WITH HER CHAOTIC HOME LIFE.

HOW ABOUT SOMETHING TO WEAR?

HEAVENS NO. SHE'LL THINK I'M ATTACKING THE RIDICULOUS GET-UPS SHE SPENDS HER MONEY ON.

IT'S IMPOSSIBLE TO SHOP FOR SOMEONE WHO'S SO CRITICAL!

HEY, CATHY! WHAT ARE YOU DOING IN THE MEN'S SECTION?

JUST BROWSING.

WANT ME TO RING THAT UP NOW?

YOU'RE NOT SPENDING MONEY ON IRVING, ARE YOU?

DON'T BE SILLY.

IRVING'S GOING TO LOVE THIS!!

CATHY, HOW COULD YOU??

IT'S CHEAP, ANDREA. IT'S VERY CHEAP.

THAT'LL BE $45.95! YOUR TOTAL IS $45.95!!

I HAVE TO DO SOMETHING TO MAKE MY JOB INTERESTING.

LET'S SEE... BOB MURPHY MADE A KILLING IN THE VIDEO GAME MARKET LAST YEAR...

Merry Merry Christmas

HIS WIFE BETSY OPENED HER OWN FRANCHISED CHAIN OF CREPE SHOPS... LITTLE SUSIE MURPHY GOT HER DOCTORATE AND HAD TWINS...

...BOTH OF WHOM SPEAK FLUENT FRENCH AT 8 MONTHS. ......ISN'T THAT WONDERFUL?! NOW, WHO'S READY FOR SOME MORE PIE?

Merry Merry Christmas

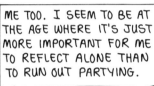

DO YOU KNOW WHY I NEVER LOSE WEIGHT, MOM? IT'S BECAUSE OF THAT DISAPPROVING LOOK YOU GET ON YOUR FACE.

THERE'S NOTHING WRONG WITH ME EATING **ONE** COOKIE...BUT WHEN YOU GIVE ME THAT LOOK, I GET NERVOUS AND DEFENSIVE AND THEN I WANT TO EAT THE WHOLE BOX!

FINE. WHY DON'T I JUST LEAVE THE ROOM?

I CAN FEEL YOUR DISAPPROVING LOOK THROUGH THE WALL!!

OF COURSE YOU DON'T HAVE TO WATCH OVER ME, ANDREA, I'M IN CONTROL OF MY DIET THIS TIME!

I'VE SET REALISTIC GOALS, AND I'M WORKING TOWARDS THEM SLOWLY AND SENSIBLY!

I'M PROUD OF YOU, CATHY. KEEP UP THE GOOD WORK!

SLAM!

PEOPLE WHO HAVE A CHEESECAKE IN THE REFRIGERATOR WILL SAY ANYTHING.

I LOVE GOING GROCERY SHOPPING WHEN I'M STILL DRESSED IN MY OFFICE CLOTHES.

I FEEL SO PROFESSIONAL... ...SO EFFICIENT...

I CAN'T GET THESE STUPID PLASTIC BAGS OPEN!!

...SO DYNAMIC... SO RESPECTABLE...

I'M GOING TO THROW THE REST OF THE COOKIES DOWN THE GARBAGE DISPOSAL AND NEVER EAT ANOTHER FATTENING THING!

EAT EAT EAT EAT

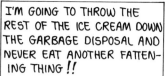

I'M GOING TO THROW THE REST OF THE ICE CREAM DOWN THE GARBAGE DISPOSAL AND NEVER EAT ANOTHER FATTENING THING!!

THIS CEREMONY IS STARTING TO LOSE ITS MEANING.

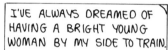

EXCITING NEWS, CATHY. I'VE HIRED AN ASSISTANT FOR YOU.

OH, MR. PINKLEY, THIS IS WONDERFUL!

I'VE ALWAYS DREAMED OF HAVING A BRIGHT YOUNG WOMAN BY MY SIDE TO TRAIN.

SHE WILL BECOME MY CONFIDANTE! I WILL BE HER MENTOR! TOGETHER, WE'LL...

THIS IS ZEKE. HE STARTS TODAY.

ZEKE?...UH, HOW DO YOU DO...

MY DESK IS TOO SMALL. THE COFFEE'S TERRIBLE. AND I WANTED AN OFFICE WITH A WINDOW.

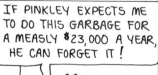

IF PINKLEY EXPECTS ME TO DO THIS GARBAGE FOR A MEASLY $23,000 A YEAR, HE CAN FORGET IT!

$23,000 A YEAR? MY ASSISTANT IS MAKING $23,000 A YEAR??!

MR. PINKLEY, ISN'T THERE SOMETHING YOU'D LIKE TO SAY ABOUT THIS??

YOU PROMISED NOT TO TELL!!

I KNOW I SHOULD GIVE MR. PINKLEY A BIG LECTURE ...BUT LET'S FACE IT, ANDREA, CRYING **WORKS**. IT'S A DECISION WE ALL HAVE TO MAKE.

DO WE CONFRONT SITUATIONS WITH INTELLIGENCE AND DIGNITY, OR DO WE RESORT TO THE CHEAP--BUT EFFECTIVE--TACTIC OF TEARS?

MR. PINKLEY, I... **WAAAAH!!**

MY INSTINCTS TOOK OVER.

ON JANUARY 1, MY GOAL WAS TO LOSE 15 POUNDS AND GET EVERY ASPECT OF MY LIFE ORGANIZED TO PERFECTION.

ON JANUARY 7, MY GOAL WAS TO HAVE A SEMBLANCE OF ORDER AND PERIODIC SELF-DISCIPLINE.

TODAY, 16 DAYS INTO THE NEW YEAR, I'M CLINGING TO THE SHREDS OF 23-SELF-IMPROVEMENT PROJECTS AND MY ONLY GOAL IS TO NOT WAKE UP WITH A HEADACHE.

YOU'RE AMAZING, CATHY.

I KNOW. THIS IS THE BEST I'VE EVER DONE.

WOMEN WERE CONDITIONED FOR TWO RESPONSES, MR. PINKLEY. WE SMILE OR WE CRY.

EVEN WHEN WE'RE FURIOUS, WE EXPRESS IT BY CRYING OR SMILING.

I JUST WANT YOU TO KNOW THAT UNDER THIS CHEERY SMILE IS THE HEART OF A WOMAN WHO WANTS TO RIP YOUR FACE OFF FOR PAYING MY ASSISTANT $23,000 A YEAR.

WHAT DO YOU MEAN, HE DIDN'T TAKE YOU SERIOUSLY?

A mouthful
of breath mints
and no one to kiss

A mouthful of breath mints and no one to kiss

by Cathy Guisewite

Andrews and McMeel, Inc.
A Universal Press Syndicate Company
Kansas City ● New York

A  Collection

PART OF ME DOESN'T EVEN CARE ABOUT VALENTINE'S DAY THIS YEAR...ANOTHER PART OF ME WANTS AN APARTMENT FULL OF CARDS AND FLOWERS...

PART OF ME THINKS VALENTINE'S DAY IS A CHEAP, COMMERCIALIZED EVENT... ANOTHER PART OF ME IS SCREAMING FOR PINK DOILIES AND POETRY...

PART OF ME DOESN'T NEED MY SELF-ESTEEM RAISED BY A VALENTINE... ANOTHER PART OF ME WOULD BEG AND GROVEL FOR ANYTHING WITH A HEART ON IT.

I'LL HAVE THE NACHOS FOR SIX.

QUICK! I ATE THE BOX OF CHOCOLATE MY BOYFRIEND GAVE ME FOR VALENTINE'S DAY AND I HAVE TO REPLACE IT BEFORE HE COMES OVER AND SEES THE EMPTY BOX!

½ price Valentines

QUICK! I ATE THE BOX OF CHOCOLATE I GOT TO REPLACE THE BOX MY BOYFRIEND GOT ME AND I HAVE TO REPLACE IT AGAIN!

½ price Valentines

QUICK! I ATE THE BOX OF CHOCOLATE I GOT TO REPLACE THE BOX THAT REPLACED THE BOX MY BOYFRIEND GAVE ME AND I NEED ANOTHER ONE!!

½ price Valentines

...SORRY I CAN'T MAKE IT OVER, CATHY. I HAVE TO GO OUT OF TOWN FOR A WEEK.

I MIGHT NOT GET A CHANCE TO CALL YOU FROM BOSTON, CATHY, BUT I'LL BE BACK NEXT WEEK. I LOVE YOU.

WHAT?

I'LL BE BACK NEXT WEEK. I LOVE YOU.

YOU WHAT? YOU LOVE ME? IRVING, WHERE ARE YOU?

I'M STANDING IN THE AIRPORT. OOPS. GOTTA GO. BYE.

WHY DON'T YOU EVER SAY YOU LOVE ME WHEN YOU'RE STANDING IN MY LIVING ROOM?!!

HI. I'M DANIEL. HOW DO YOU FEEL ABOUT THE WHOLE MEN/WOMEN THING?

ARE YOUR BELIEFS STRONGER THAN YOUR ACTIONS OR VICE VERSA? IF YOU HAD A DAUGHTER RIGHT NOW, WOULD YOU CONSIDER YOURSELF A GOOD ROLE MODEL?

WHICH AUTHORS HAVE BEST CAPTURED HOW YOU FEEL? ARE YOUR RELATIONSHIPS MORE COMPLICATED NOW AND IF SO, IS IT PARTLY BECAUSE IT'S HARDER TO SAY YOU NEED SOMEONE WITHOUT APPEARING TO BE A HYPOCRITE?

WHATEVER HAPPENED TO "HELLO, BEAUTIFUL. WHAT'S YOUR SIGN?"

YES, OF COURSE, MR. PINKLEY.

NO PROBLEM. I'M SURE THE TIME YOU SPEND WILL ULTIMATELY BE A BENEFIT TO THE CORPORATE IMAGE.

CERTAINLY... AS THE HEAD OF THIS DIVISION, IT'S CRUCIAL FOR YOU TO STAY ON TOP OF NEW DEVELOPMENTS SUCH AS THIS. I UNDERSTAND.

MR. PINKLEY WILL BE A LITTLE LATE TODAY. HE'S HAVING HIS COLORS DONE.

WHAT DOES "CRAB BORDELAISE" MEAN?

IT'S FRENCH FOR CELLULITE.

MOM, IF YOU'RE UPSET ABOUT SOMETHING, WOULD YOU JUST SAY WHAT IT IS?!

WELL. AREN'T WE GROUCHY TODAY?

I'M NOT GROUCHY. I JUST WISH YOU'D OPEN UP AND SAY WHAT'S ON YOUR MIND FOR ONCE!!

WHAT'LL IT BE, LADIES?

THE CRAB AND THE CLAM.

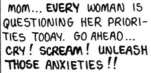

MY FRIEND OLLIE WROTE TO THE GOVERNMENT FOR INFORMATION ON SMALL BUSINESS SUBSIDIES.

FLO ORDERED BROCHURES ON SETTING UP SMALL BUSINESSES AND FINANCING BUSINESSES. HELEN SENT IN FOR "SMALL BUSINESS STRATEGIES", "BUSINESS STATISTICS" AND "YOUR BUSINESS AND YOU".

TOMORROW WE'RE GOING TO SIT DOWN AND START TURNING OUR DREAMS INTO REALITY!

GOOD FOR YOU, MOM!

WE HAVE TO. WE RAN OUT OF THINGS TO SEND AWAY FOR.

FLO, WE HAVE GATHERED HERE TO DISCUSS NEW BUSINESS OPPORTUNITIES... NOT TO LISTEN TO YOU GLOAT ABOUT YOUR GRANDDAUGHTER.

IF YOU WHIP OUT THAT PHOTO ALBUM ONE MORE TIME, I WILL HAVE NO CHOICE BUT TO DISMISS YOU FROM THIS AND ALL FURTHER SESSIONS... ALL IN FAVOR, SAY "AYE!"

OH, SHE'S ADORABLE ...OOH, LOOK AT THIS ONE

OOH... ISN'T THAT SWEET... AW...

MOVE OVER, OLLIE.

IF YOUR CATHY WERE MARRIED LIKE MY DAUGHTERS...

FLO, I HAPPEN TO BE VERY PROUD OF CATHY'S INDEPENDENCE

WHEN AND IF SHE DECIDES TO MARRY AND HAVE A FAMILY, SHE WILL BE DOING SO ON A SOLID FOUNDATION OF CONFIDENCE AND SELF-RESPECT!

MOM, I COULDN'T HELP OVERHEARING WHAT YOU SAID. THAT WAS BEAUTIFUL!

WHERE ARE MY GRANDCHILDREN??

FLO, WAIT! COME BACK!

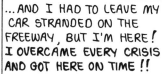

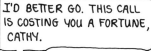

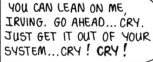

HI, IRVING. WOULD YOU MIND PICKING UP MY DRY CLEANING TODAY?

CATHY, JUST BECAUSE I'M NOT GOING INTO A REGULAR OFFICE DOESN'T MEAN I HAVE NOTHING TO DO.

I HAVE INTERVIEWS TO SET UP...CALLS TO MAKE...RESUMES TO PREPARE... I DO NOT HAVE TIME TO RUN AROUND DOING YOUR ERRANDS!

PEOPLE WHO WORK AT HOME GET NO RESPECT.

CLICK!

I'D LIKE A BREATH MINT, BUT I DON'T WANT TO BE SO OBVIOUS ABOUT PREPARING FOR A BIG KISS AT THE DOOR.

I COULD OFFER HIM A BREATH MINT, BUT THEN I'D BE REALLY OBVIOUS... I COULD TRY TO SECRETLY EAT A BREATH MINT, BUT THAT WOULD BE REALLY, REALLY OBVIOUS... I...

BYE, CATHY. SEE YOU SOON.

THE STORY OF MY LIFE. A MOUTHFUL OF BREATH MINTS, AND NO ONE TO KISS.

EVERYWHERE YOU GO, THERE'S TOO MUCH STUFF TO BUY. I WENT TO THE DRUGSTORE FOR A TUBE OF TOOTHPASTE, I CAME OUT WITH A DINETTE SET.

I WENT TO THE GAS STATION FOR GAS, I CAME HOME WITH A 5-PIECE LUGGAGE ENSEMBLE.

I WENT TO THE CARD SHOP FOR A CARD, I CAME AWAY WITH AN ESPRESSO MACHINE. YOUR FATHER IS JUST GOING TO KILL ME.

WHERE IS DAD?

HE RAN OUT FOR A NEWSPAPER.

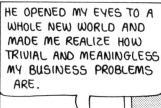

MY BLUE SKIRT AND MY TAN JACKET ARE GETTING DRY CLEANED.

MY GREEN DRESS IS HAVING A NEW ZIPPER PUT IN. MY LAVENDER BLOUSE IS WAITING FOR BUTTONS.

MY WHITE SLACKS AND ALL MY UNDERWEAR ARE IN THE WASHING MACHINE.

I WON'T BE IN TODAY, MR. PINKLEY. MY CLOTHES ARE ALL BUSY.

I KNOW UNEMPLOYMENT IS HARD ON YOU, IRVING, BUT I DON'T WANT IT TO DRIVE US APART.

YOUR TRIUMPHS ARE **OUR** TRIUMPHS...YOUR DISASTERS ARE **OUR** DISASTERS...

IRVING, IF WE CAN JUST LEARN TO SHARE, NOTHING WILL EVER COME BETWEEN US!!

RING RING

...IT'S OUR OTHER GIRLFRIEND.

14 RINGS...15 RINGS... COME ON, IRVING, ANSWER YOUR PHONE.

RING! RING!

19...20...21...I KNOW YOU'RE THERE, IRVING, AND I'M GOING TO LET IT RING UNTIL I TALK TO YOU!

RING! RING!

CATHY, EXACTLY HOW GOOD OF A CONVERSATION DO YOU EXPECT TO HAVE WITH A MAN WHO'S LET HIS PHONE RING 26 TIMES BEFORE ANSWERING IT??

RING RING RING

....HELLO?

GLFKT.

YOU MADE ME NERVOUS.

NO, I WILL NOT STAY LATE AGAIN, MR. PINKLEY. MY PERSONAL RELATIONSHIPS ARE UNDER A BIG ENOUGH STRAIN WITHOUT ADDING ANOTHER MIDNIGHT AT THE OFFICE.

IF YOU CONTINUE TO MAKE THESE OUTRAGEOUS DEMANDS, YOU'RE GOING TO HAVE TO JUST FIND YOURSELF ANOTHER SLAVE!

IT'S HARD TO BELIEVE I PUT MY CAREER ON THE LINE FOR A "THREE'S COMPANY" RERUN.

WELL, UM, MAYBE WE CAN GET TOGETHER SOMETIME, CATHY...MAYBE I'LL GIVE YOU A CALL NEXT WEEK... MAYBE WE'LL GET SOME DINNER...WELL, MAYBE. WE'LL SEE...

MEN ARE LUNATICS, ANDREA.

YOU JUST EXPECT TOO MUCH, CATHY.

WHEN ARE YOU GOING TO REALIZE THERE'S NO SUCH THING AS "MR. RIGHT"?

ANDREA, I KNOW THERE'S NO SUCH THING AS MR. RIGHT.

...THEY'RE ALL MR. MAYBE'S.

I'M WEARING "THE PROVOCATIVE NEW COLOGNE FOR WOMEN." HE'S WEARING "THE DARING NEW MEN'S COLOGNE."

THE ROOM IS CHARGED WITH ELECTRICITY.

I THINK OUR COLOGNES ARE HAVING A PARTY IN MID-AIR.

YOU HEARD ME, IRVING. I WANT LIVER FOR DINNER.

EVERY TIME YOU FEEL GUILTY ABOUT SOMETHING, YOU START WORRYING ABOUT YOUR NUTRITION.

YOU FIGURE YOU'LL FEEL BETTER ABOUT HAVING ME SECRETLY STAYING HERE IF YOU EAT A DINNER YOUR MOTHER WOULD APPROVE OF.

YOU'RE NUTS, CATHY! NOBODY IN THE WORLD IS AS NUTS AS YOU ARE!!

AT LEAST I KNOW SHE'S EATING RIGHT.

HOW DID YOU FIND OUT THAT IRVING IS STAYING AT MY APARTMENT, MOM?

FLO TOLD ME.

FLO TOLD ME. FLO TOLD HER NEIGHBORS. HER NEIGHBORS TOLD THEIR CO-WORKERS.

THEIR CO-WORKERS ALERTED ALL THEIR RELATIVES, WHO SET UP A COAST-TO-COAST HOTLINE...AND FOR THOSE WHO MISSED OUT, STAY TUNED FOR THE 6:00 NEWS!

...THAT'S THE LAST TIME I ASK FLO TO SNEAK OVER TO YOUR PLACE AND FIND OUT WHAT'S GOING ON.

IRVING, YOUR DIRTY DISHES ARE IN MY SINK!

SO WHAT, CATHY? SO ARE YOURS!!

I DON'T WANT YOUR DIRTY DISHES TOUCHING MY DIRTY DISHES!!

YEAH? WELL, I DON'T WANT YOUR GARBAGE TOUCHING MY GARBAGE!!

THAT'S MY PAPER TOWEL! DON'T TOUCH MY PAPER TOWEL!!

IF MOTHERS ONLY KNEW HOW LITTLE THEY HAD TO WORRY ABOUT...

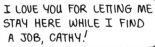

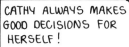
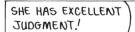

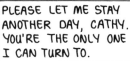

PLEASE LET ME STAY ANOTHER DAY, CATHY. YOU'RE THE ONLY ONE I CAN TURN TO.

OH, NO. I'M NOT FALLING FOR THAT OLD LINE AGAIN.

PLEASE LET ME STAY, CATHY. I WILL NEVER TAKE OUR FRIENDSHIP FOR GRANTED AGAIN.

OH, NO. I'M NOT FALLING FOR THAT OLD LINE AGAIN.

PLEASE LET ME STAY, CATHY. BY HELPING ME, YOU'RE DOING YOUR PART TOWARDS RESTORING ORDER TO THESE TIMES OF ECONOMICAL AND EMOTIONAL CHAOS.

OKAY.

I HADN'T HEARD THAT ONE YET.

MY NEW BOYFRIEND ISN'T SPEAKING TO ME, MY MOM ISN'T SPEAKING TO ME, MY EX-BOYFRIEND IS ASLEEP ON MY COUCH AND I JUST GAINED 8 POUNDS.

OH, CATHY...

THEN AGAIN, MAYBE IT'S NOT SO BAD... SOMETIMES YOU HAVE TO FEEL TERRIBLE BEFORE YOU CAN BE MOTIVATED TO CHANGE SOMETHING.

SOMETIMES YOU CAN ONLY TURN YOUR LIFE AROUND AFTER YOU'VE REALLY HIT THE BOTTOM!

IN WHAT WAY IS A QUART OF ICE CREAM GOING TO HELP?

I'M NOT QUITE LOW ENOUGH.

AREN'T YOU NERVOUS ABOUT IRVING SNOOPING AROUND ALL YOUR STUFF WHILE YOU'RE AT WORK ALL DAY, CATHY?

ANDREA, IRVING AND I HAVE ALWAYS BEEN TOTALLY OPEN ABOUT OUR OTHER FRIENDSHIPS.

I HAVE NOTHING TO HIDE!!

GOOD FOR YOU! AND **WHY** DON'T YOU HAVE ANYTHING TO HIDE?!

I ALREADY HID EVERYTHING.

IRVING, YOU AND I BOTH NEEDED A PLACE TO STAY, AND WE BOTH PICKED CATHY'S LIVING ROOM.

I THINK WE SHOULD TALK ABOUT THIS. LET'S GET OUR FEELINGS OUT IN THE OPEN!

IT IS EXACTLY THESE AWKWARD MOMENTS THAT CAN BRING US CLOSER TO THE REAL TRUTHS IN HUMAN RELATIONSHIPS!!

NEVER BUY TWO MEN YOU'RE DATING THE SAME SWEATER FOR CHRISTMAS.

I'M IRVING. WHO ARE YOU?

PHILLIP. I USED TO GO OUT WITH CATHY. MIND IF I HAVE A SEAT UNTIL SHE GETS HOME FROM WORK?

I'M DAVID. WHO ARE YOU?

EMERSON. I USED TO GO OUT WITH CATHY. MIND IF I HAVE A SEAT UNTIL SHE GETS HOME FROM WORK?

WHO ARE YOU?

MARK. I USED TO GO OUT WITH CATHY. MIND IF I HAVE A SEAT UNTIL SHE GETS HOME FROM WORK?

WHEW! AFTER A DAY LIKE TODAY, THINGS CAN ONLY GET BETTER.

EVERY PERSON I'VE EVER DATED IN MY LIFE IS STANDING IN MY LIVING ROOM, ANDREA.

OH, CATHY...

WHY DOES THIS ALWAYS HAPPEN?? EITHER THERE'S NO ONE, OR ELSE EVERYONE IN THE WORLD SHOWS UP AT THE SAME TIME!

CATHY, THIS IS HORRIBLE! YOU HAVE TO DO SOMETHING!

REFRESHMENTS! I'LL GO TO THE STORE AND BUY SOME REFRESHMENTS!!

SUPERMARKET

SALE

SALE

donuts

DAVID WENT BACK TO ST. LOUIS AND IRVING MOVED IN WITH HIS PARENTS. AT LEAST MY MOTHER WILL BE THRILLED.

IT WAS HORRIBLE TO SEE THEM LEAVE...BUT I JUST KEPT THINKING, "MOM IS GOING TO BE THRILLED".

SOME THINGS ARE WORTH GOING THROUGH IF ONLY BECAUSE YOU KNOW YOUR MOTHER WILL BE TOTALLY THRILLED!

...WHATEVER MAKES YOU HAPPY, DEAR.

RELATIONSHIPS ARE LIKE A GIANT PLATE OF SPAGHETTI, ANDREA.

EACH PIECE IS PERFECT BY ITSELF... BUT WHEN YOU PUT IT ALL TOGETHER, IT BECOMES A TANGLED MESS, IMPOSSIBLE TO SORT OUT.

VERY INTERESTING, CATHY.

USING THAT SAME THEORY, WE SEE THAT RELATIONSHIPS ARE ALSO LIKE A TINY TOSSED SALAD... AFTER BEING PART OF THE WHOLE, NO ONE PIECE IS EVER EXACTLY THE SAME.

DON'T BE RIDICULOUS.

"AMAZING NEW DIET BREAKTHROUGH! LOSE 15 POUNDS IN 7 DAYS!"

HA! WHAT TRASH!!

GOOD FOR YOU, CATHY. YOU'RE FINALLY GETTING MORE REALISTIC ABOUT YOUR WEIGHT LOSS PROGRAMS!

I NEED TO FIND ONE WHERE I CAN LOSE 15 POUNDS IN 3 DAYS.

CRASH!

SPLAT! GZKKK...

I WON'T BE IN TODAY, MR. PINKLEY. I DON'T THINK I SHOULD BE ALLOWED NEAR A CAR.

I THOUGHT YOU INVITED ME OVER TO SCREAM AT ME, CATHY.

I DID, IRVING.

...BUT LISTEN TO THAT SONG ON THE RADIO. REMEMBER HOW HAPPY WE WERE WHEN THAT SONG FIRST CAME OUT?

YOU'RE NOT GOING TO SCREAM AT ME?

NOW THEY'RE PLAYING OUR OTHER FAVORITE SONG! OH, IRVING! IRVING!!

KISS KISS KISS KISS KISS

WHERE'S THE REST OF THE COFFEE, MOM?

I DON'T KNOW. I MADE 3 CUPS.

MOM, "3 CUPS" ON THAT COFFEE MAKER DOESN'T EVEN FILL ONE MUG.

AT MY HOUSE "3 CUPS" MAKES 3 CUPS.

AT YOUR HOUSE YOU USE PUNY CUPS. IF YOU WANT TO MAKE 3 CONTEMPORARY MUGS OF COFFEE, YOU HAVE TO MAKE 7 CUPS!

7 CUPS! WE'LL NEVER FINISH 7 CUPS!!

HOW'S YOUR MOM?

I DON'T KNOW. BY THE TIME WE SAT DOWN TO TALK, WE WEREN'T SPEAKING TO EACH OTHER.

CHARLENE SPENT THE MORNING COMPLAINING ABOUT THE FACT THAT MORRIE NEVER CLEANS UP THE COFFEE ROOM.

THEN JOANN ACCUSED TIM OF STEALING HER IDEAS FOR THE DRAPE PROJECT... THEN BETH ANNOUNCED SHE WAS GOING TO QUIT IF SUE DIDN'T QUIT HOGGING THE WHITE-OUT.

NOW IT'S 4:30 AND YOU'VE BEEN WAITING TO HAVE A MEETING WITH ME ALL DAY... WHAT DID YOU WANT TO DISCUSS, MR. PINKLEY?

CARLA CALLED ME "FATTY"!!

WHY DON'T YOU EVER INVITE ME TO YOUR BUSINESS DINNERS, CATHY?

IRVING, HONEY, IF YOU CAME, I'D SPEND THE WHOLE EVENING WORRYING ABOUT WHETHER OR NOT YOU WERE ENJOYING YOURSELF.

"WHAT'S IRVING THINKING ABOUT?"... "DOES HE FEEL LEFT OUT?"... "IS HE THREATENED?"...

FORGET IT, CATHY. FORGET I EVEN BROUGHT IT UP!!

...WHAT'S IRVING THINKING ABOUT?... DOES HE FEEL LEFT OUT?... IS HE THREATENED?...

I KNOW IRVING AND I ARE TOTALLY DIFFERENT PEOPLE, ANDREA... BUT WE KEEP COMING BACK TO EACH OTHER.

DEEP DOWN, I THINK WE BOTH WANT EXACTLY THE SAME THING!

WE BOTH WANT THE OTHER PERSON TO CHANGE.

ROOM SERVICE.

HI. I'D LIKE TO ORDER BREAKFAST. HOW LONG WILL IT TAKE?

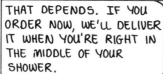

THAT DEPENDS. IF YOU ORDER NOW, WE'LL DELIVER IT WHEN YOU'RE RIGHT IN THE MIDDLE OF YOUR SHOWER.

HOWEVER, IF YOU ORDER BREAKFAST AFTER YOUR SHOWER, WE'LL WAIT TO BRING IT UNTIL 4 SECONDS BEFORE YOU HAVE TO LEAVE FOR YOUR MEETING.

COULDN'T YOU JUST PLAN TO BRING IT 20 MINUTES FROM NOW?

DON'T BE RIDICULOUS. WE CAN'T TIME THINGS THAT EXACTLY.

THANKS FOR DINNER AND FOR NOT TRYING TO KISS ME, RALPH.

NO PROBLEM. I HAVE A WHOLE NEW RESPECT FOR MY FEMALE BUSINESS ASSOCIATES.

YOU MADE ME REALIZE HOW TACKY IT IS TO EXPECT A KISS IN RETURN FOR BUYING YOU A $50 BUSINESS DINNER.

INSTEAD, YOU CAN REPAY ME BY GIVING AN INFORMAL 45-MINUTE TALK TO 50 OF OUR SALES PEOPLE AT 8:00 TOMORROW MORNING.

EVERY NOW AND THEN, I HATE PROGRESS.

HI, CATHY. HOW'S YOUR TRIP?

AT 10:00 TONIGHT MY CLIENT TOLD ME I WAS SUPPOSED TO GIVE A 45-MINUTE TALK AT 8:00 TOMORROW MORNING, ANDREA.

THEY ONLY GAVE ME ONE NIGHT TO PREPARE A 45-MINUTE TALK FOR 50 PEOPLE!!

ONE NIGHT TO PREPARE WHAT COULD BE THE MOST IMPORTANT PRESENTATION OF MY ENTIRE CAREER!!

OH, CATHY...WHAT ARE YOU GOING TO DO?!

I DECIDED TO GET UP EARLY AND DO IT IN THE MORNING.

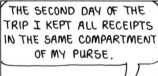

DEAR FLOYD,
WE ARE SICK AND TIRED OF YOUR OUTRAGEOUS DEMANDS. AS FAR AS I'M CONCERNED, YOU CAN TAKE YOUR BUSINESS AND...

DEAR FLOYD,
THIS IS THE LAST TIME PRODUCT TESTING INC. IS GOING TO CATER TO ONE OF YOUR LUDICROUS EMERGENCIES. IN THE...

DEAR FLOYD,
ENCLOSED ARE THE PROJECTS YOU REQUESTED. BEST WISHES, CATHY.

A GOOD BUSINESS LETTER TAKES SEVERAL DRAFTS.

I'M LOST.

WHAT DO YOU MEAN, YOU'RE LOST, CATHY?

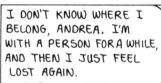
I DON'T KNOW WHERE I BELONG, ANDREA. I'M WITH A PERSON FOR A WHILE, AND THEN I JUST FEEL LOST AGAIN.

EVEN WHEN PEOPLE SAY, "I NEVER WANT TO LOSE YOU," I ALWAYS WIND UP FEELING LOST.

THIS MUST BE WHAT IT FEELS LIKE TO BE A PAIR OF SUNGLASSES.

WHAT DO YOU WANT TO DO IN THE NEXT FIVE YEARS, CATHY?

YOU WERE ALWAYS ON MY MIND... YOU WERE ALWAYS ON MY MIND...

I WOULD LIKE TO SPEND THE NEXT FIVE YEARS STARING AT YOUR GORGEOUS FACE.

I'M SORRY... I COULDN'T HEAR YOU OVER THE MUSIC.

...TELL ME THAT OUR SWEET LOVE HASN'T DIE O...

UM... I'D LIKE TO SPEND THE NEXT FIVE YEARS EXPLORING THE MANY FASCINATING ASPECTS OF MY CAREER.

OH.

ANOTHER RELATIONSHIP GETS DROWNED OUT BY A LOVE SONG.

HOW COULD CHARLENE MARRY A MAN LIKE FRANK? I THOUGHT SHE'D MADE MORE PROGRESS THAN THAT.

CATHY, FRANK IS EXACTLY THE TYPE OF GUY THAT IRVING IS, AND YOU'VE DATED HIM FOR 5 YEARS!

WHAT PROGRESS DO YOU THINK *YOU'VE* MADE ??

I'M LESS TOLERANT OF MY FRIENDS' RELATIONSHIPS.

BZZZ BZZZ BZZZZZ BZZZZ

YOU'RE STILL HERE ??

DON'T YOU HAVE ANYWHERE ELSE TO GO? DON'T YOU HAVE SOMETHING ELSE TO DO ??

BZZZ "00" BZZZZ BZZZ

YOU HAVE THE WHOLE WORLD TO PICK FROM !! WHY ARE YOU TORTURING *ME* ??

BZZZZ "00" BZZZ BZZZZ

COMPANY ALWAYS STAYS TOO LONG IN AUGUST.

BZZZ BZZZ BZZZ BZZZ

IRVING.....

AACK. I CAN'T SAY THAT. I'LL SOUND SO CONFUSED AND WEAK.

I *AM* CONFUSED. BUT IT'S SO EMBARRASSING TO ADMIT IT. I'M SCARED TO SAY I CARE. I'M SCARED TO SAY I DON'T.

AAAGH. THIS IS AGONY! THIS IS TORTURE TO OPEN UP TO HIM...

IRVING, I THINK WE NEED TO DISCUSS OUR RELATIONSHIP.

SURE YOU DO. IT'S SO EASY FOR WOMEN TO TALK ABOUT THEIR FEELINGS.

YOU'RE WORKING LATE? YOU PROMISED YOU'D HELP PLAN MY DINNER PARTY.

I'M SORRY, MOM. NEXT WEEK I'LL COOK THE WHOLE DINNER AND HELP YOU CLEAN YOUR ENTIRE HOUSE.

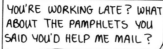

YOU'RE WORKING LATE? WHAT ABOUT THE PAMPHLETS YOU SAID YOU'D HELP ME MAIL?

I'M SORRY, ANDREA. NEXT WEEK I'LL HAND-DELIVER THE PAMPHLETS WITH A PERSONAL NOTE OF APOLOGY TO EACH ONE.

YOU'RE WORKING LATE? I THOUGHT WE WERE GOING TO SEE A MOVIE.

I'M SORRY, IRVING. NEXT WEEK I'LL TAKE YOU TO EVERY MOVIE IN TOWN AND I'LL WAX YOUR CAR.

...JUST THINK, CATHY. WHEN THIS WEEK IS OVER, YOU CAN JUST SIT BACK AND RELAX!

IF YOU DON'T GET THE PROJECT DONE, YOU'LL UNDERMINE YOUR CLIENT'S TRUST AND RISK LOSING THE BUSINESS THAT PAYS YOUR SALARY, CATHY.

THEN AGAIN, IF YOU **DO** GET THE PROJECT DONE, YOU'LL HAVE SET A PRECEDENT FOR SPEED THAT WILL HAUNT YOU THE REST OF YOUR CAREER AND GIVE YOU A NERVOUS BREAKDOWN.

IF YOU GET THE PROJECT DONE BUT DO IT POORLY BE-CAUSE YOU'RE HURRYING, YOU'LL DEMEAN YOUR CAPA-BILITIES AND DESTROY ALL CHANCE FOR ADVANCEMENT.

I LOVE A JOB WITH AN ELEMENT OF SUSPENSE.

WELL, HERE WE ALL ARE: COFFEE TO HELP ME STAY AWAKE... COOKIES TO HELP ME WRITE...

DONUTS TO HELP ME TYPE... PRETZELS TO HELP ME PROOF-READ... CHOCOLATE TO HELP ME COLLATE...

HOW'S IT GOING, CATHY?

MY STAFF KEEPS DISAPPEARING.

THIS IS THE HOT NEW LOOK IN TWEEDY JACKETS FOR FALL...

FALL FASHION HEADS

AND THIS IS THE HOT NEW LOOK IN SKIRTS...

FALL FASHI HEAD

... PUT THEM TOGETHER WITH THE HOT NEW LOOK IN SWEATERS AND TEXTURED HOSE. IT'S HOT, HOT, HOT!

...BOY, DO YOU LOOK **HOT**, CATHY!

THANK YOU.

TICKETS

MORE SHOES? WHAT DO YOU NEED MORE SHOES FOR, CATHY?

WOMEN'S SHOES

THAT SEEMS A LITTLE RIDICULOUS COMING FROM A MAN WHO OWNS 132 SHIRTS, IRVING.

WOMEN'

...NOT TO MENTION THE FACT THAT MEN'S SHIRTS ESSENTIALLY STAY IN STYLE FOR YEARS, WHEREAS WOMEN'S SHOES CHANGE RADICALLY EACH SEASON... THE QUALITY AND CUT OF WHICH ARE OFTEN THE BASIS BY WHICH A WOMAN'S ENTIRE PRESENCE IS JUDGED!

I HATE IT WHEN THE DEFENSE IS PREPARED.

WOM SHOES

I DON'T SEE WHY YOU WON'T LET ME FIX YOU UP, CATHY.

ANDREA, WAIT! DON'T EAT THAT TUNA SALAD! IT'S ROTTEN.

IF IT'S ROTTEN, WHAT'S IT DOING IN YOUR REFRIGERATOR?

WELL, IT'S NOT **THAT** ROTTEN...I MEAN, I'VE SORT OF GOTTEN USED TO SEEING IT IN THERE.

I COME HOME FROM WORK EVERY DAY AND THERE IT IS... A FAMILIAR FACE... A FRIEND... SOMEONE TO TALK..

ARE YOU SURE YOU DON'T WANT TO GET FIXED UP?

WHO EXACTLY DO YOU KNOW?

FLOYD AND HELEN, MARGO AND JACK, AND NEIMAN-MARCUS ARE CELEBRATING THEIR ANNIVERSARIES TODAY. I'M SENDING THEM ALL A NICE CARD.

NEIMAN-MARCUS IS A STORE, MOM.

THEY'VE BEEN TOGETHER 75 YEARS!

FOR 75 YEARS THEY'VE STAYED COMMITTED TO THEIR RELATIONSHIP, UNLIKE YOU YOUNG PEOPLE TODAY WHO BREAK UP BEFORE YOU EVEN KNOW EACH OTHER'S LAST NAMES!

I GET THE POINT, MOTHER.

POINT? WHAT POINT? I WAS JUST MAKING CONVERSATION.

WHY DID I TELL PINKLEY I'D WORK ON THAT STUPID PROJECT THIS WEEKEND??

WHY CAN'T I LOSE ANY WEIGHT? WHY AREN'T I SAVING ANY MONEY? WHY DO I LISTEN TO ANDREA'S ADVICE?

AND **YOU**, IRVING! WHY DO YOU ALWAYS DISAPPEAR JUST WHEN THINGS ARE STARTING TO WORK??

CLEANING THE HOUSE CAN BE VERY THERAPEUTIC.

MR. PINKLEY SAID YOU'D FILL ME IN ON THE NEW PERSON HE HIRED FOR MY DEPARTMENT.

HE'S **SINGLE**, CATHY! SINGLE, SINGLE, SINGLE!!

CHARLENE, THIS IS **BUSINESS**. COULD YOU POSSIBLY GIVE ME A LITTLE MORE **USEFUL** INFORMATION??

SORRY.

HE'S 5'10", WITH A POWERFUL YET LEAN WARREN BEATTY BODY, A PAUL SIMON SMILE, A TUMBLE OF SUN-STREAKED WALNUT HAIR, AND EYES THE COLOR OF A 1979 STEEL BLUE MERCEDES BENZ 450 SL.

THANK YOU.

THERE. ARE 7 MILLION MORE SINGLE ADULT WOMEN IN THIS COUNTRY THAN THERE ARE SINGLE ADULT MEN.

I SPEND 99% OF MY LIFE AT WORK. HOWEVER, I'M NOT SUPPOSED TO DATE ANY-ONE IN MY COMPANY.

WHAT, THEN, IS MY CHANCE OF MEETING AN AVAILABLE, ATTRACTIVE MAN IN MY 1% OF REMAINING TIME WHO SHARES AN INTEREST IN THE THINGS I DO, YET WORKS IN A TOTALLY DIFFERENT FIELD?

... I ALWAYS KNEW THOSE STORY PROBLEMS WOULD COME BACK TO HAUNT ME.

YESTERDAY GRANT SAID THE...

CATHY, FORGET GRANT. YOU ARE NOT GOING TO DATE SOME-ONE WHO WORKS IN YOUR OFFICE.

DO YOU REALIZE HOW HIDEOUS IT WOULD BE IF YOU AND GRANT BROKE UP AND YOU STILL HAD TO SEE HIM EVERY DAY??

I BROKE UP WITH **IRVING** 5 YEARS AGO, AND I STILL SEE **HIM** EVERY DAY.

I REST MY CASE.

I'M GLAD YOU CHANGED YOUR MIND ABOUT DATING SOMEONE AT WORK.

THIS ISN'T A DATE, GRANT. WE'RE SIT-TING IN MY OFFICE.

CATHY, IT'S 9:00 AT NIGHT, WE'RE EATING DINNER, BRUCE SPRINGSTEEN IS SING-ING IN THE BACKGROUND, AND WE'RE TALKING ABOUT THE PEOPLE WE'RE GOING TO GO OUT WITH.

YES, AND UNFORTUNATELY, SINCE WE'RE NOT GETTING ANYTHING DONE, WE'RE GOING TO HAVE TO WORK LATE AGAIN TOMORROW NIGHT!

OH, DARN.

DARN, DARN DARN...

YOU'RE FINALLY CLEANING OUT THIS CLOSET??

WELL, I THOUGHT, WHAT IF GRANT ASKS ME OUT AND I SAY "YES".

THEN WHAT IF WE HAVE SUCH A WONDERFUL TIME THAT HE BEGS TO COME OVER AND FIX ME DINNER THIS WEEK-END... AND WHILE HE COOKS, I LEAN OVER AND WHISPER ENDEARING THINGS IN HIS EAR...

FLUSTERED BY MY COOL CHARM, HE KNOCKS THE HOLLANDAISE SAUCE ON THE FLOOR AND GOES LOOKING FOR A RAG TO CLEAN IT UP... IF THAT HAPPENED, I WOULD WANT THIS CLOSET TO BE NICE AND NEAT.

THIS IS PATHETIC, CATHY.

IT'S GETTING THE CLOSET CLEAN, ISN'T IT?

SOMEONE FROM THE OFFICE IS GOING TO SEE US HERE, GRANT.

YOU'RE SO PARANOID, CATHY.

YOU'RE NOT PARANOID?

CATHY, I DON'T CARE WHAT ANYONE IN THE OFFICE THINKS.

SO WHAT IF THEY SEE US?? LET THEM SEE US! LOOK!! CATHY AND GRANT ARE...

EXCUSE ME...

READY TO ORDER, SWEETHEART?

WHAT MAKES YOU SUCH AN EXPERT ON DATING SOMEONE AT THE OFFICE, MOM?

I SAW IT ON THE PHIL DONAHUE SHOW.

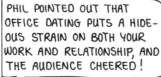

PHIL POINTED OUT THAT OFFICE DATING PUTS A HIDEOUS STRAIN ON BOTH YOUR WORK AND RELATIONSHIP, AND THE AUDIENCE CHEERED!

THEN PHIL SAID, "BUT COULDN'T A LOVING, DISCREET COUPLE MAKE IT WORK?", AND THE AUDIENCE CHEERED THAT... THEN PHIL GOT EXASPERATED BECAUSE THE SAME PEOPLE KEPT CHEERING FOR OPPOSITE THINGS, AND THE AUDIENCE CHEERED THAT! THEN...

WHAT'S YOUR POINT, MOM?

I FORGOT.

LAURA WAS BEAUTIFUL... I WANT TO MEET SOMEONE AS BEAUTIFUL AS LAURA, AND AS BRIGHT AS MAUREEN.

I'M BEAUTIFUL. I'M BRIGHT.

I WANT SOMEONE AS WITTY AS JOAN, AS SENSITIVE AS KAREN, AS CHARMING AS SUE.

I'M WITTY. I'M SENSITIVE. I'M CHARMING.

I WANT...

ME! WHAT ABOUT ME? YOU IDIOT! ME! ME!!

NAH. TOO HYSTERICAL.

THIS IS WHAT MEN HATE, CATHY. I WENT WITH YOU A COUPLE OF TIMES, AND SUDDENLY YOU'RE MAKING ME FEEL THE PRESSURE OF A WHOLE RELATIONSHIP.

WE DON'T **HAVE** A RELATIONSHIP. WE HAD TWO GREAT DATES. WHO KNOWS? MAYBE WE'LL GO OUT AGAIN.

BUT UNTIL WE DO, I AM NOT GOING TO KISS THE GROUND YOU WALK ON, OR FEEL SOME HUGE GUILT BECAUSE I'M NOT DANCING THROUGH EVERY MOMENT OF MY LIFE WITH YOU!

WHAT DID GRANT SAY?

"GREAT DATES. GO OUT AGAIN. KISS AND DANCE."

IN THE 70'S WE USED TO LEAP INTO LOVE BUT THEN DENY THAT WE WERE INVOLVED.

NOW IT'S THE 80'S. WE TALK ABOUT HOW MUCH WE **WANT** TO GET INVOLVED, BUT WE STAY A MILE AWAY FROM AN ACTUAL RELATIONSHIP.

WERE WE BETTER OFF CARING AND PRETENDING WE DIDN'T, OR ARE WE BETTER OFF ADMITTING WE WANT TO CARE, EVEN THOUGH WE RUN WHEN THE OPPORTUNITY PRESENTS ITSELF?

...THIS MAY BE A TWO-CAKE QUESTION.

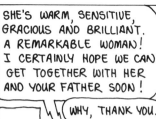

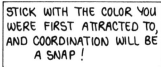

IT'S 8:00, CATHY. AREN'T YOU GOING HOME TONIGHT?

NOT YET, CHARLENE. I HAVE SO MUCH WORK TO DO!

REPORTS TO PREPARE... NUMBERS TO GO OVER... DICTATING TO CATCH UP ON... I COULD BE HERE FOREVER!

GRANT ALREADY LEFT. HE SNEAKED OUT THE BACK DOOR TWO HOURS AGO.

GOODNIGHT, CHARLENE.

I ALWAYS USED TO GET MY DAD A TIE FOR HIS BIRTHDAY.

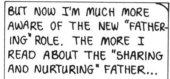

BUT NOW I'M MUCH MORE AWARE OF THE NEW "FATHERING" ROLE. THE MORE I READ ABOUT THE "SHARING AND NURTURING" FATHER...

...THE MORE I APPRECIATE THE IMPACT MY DAD HAD ON ME, AND HOW FAR AHEAD OF HIS TIME HE WAS IN THE WAY HE BROUGHT ME UP!!

SO NOW WHAT ARE YOU GOING TO GET HIM?

A TIE. BUT A MORE MEANINGFUL TIE.

I'M FURIOUS WITH GRANT ABOUT OUR DATE LAST NIGHT, BUT I DON'T WANT HIM TO THINK THAT'S WHY I'M CRITICIZING HIS REPORT.

I JUST HAVE TO BE DIGNIFIED, PROFESSIONAL, AND CHOOSE MY WORDS VERY CAREFULLY.

DRIVEL! DRIVEL! DRIVEL!!

...HM! IT WASN'T AS HARD AS I THOUGHT.

ANY MESSAGES, CHARLENE?

YES. THE ACCOUNTING DEPARTMENT THINKS YOU SHOULD APOLOGIZE TO GRANT, BUT PERSONNEL THINKS IT WAS ALL HIS FAULT.

MANAGEMENT IS DIVIDED: 3 ON YOUR SIDE, 3 ON GRANT'S. CLERICAL IS BEHIND YOU ALL THE WAY, EXCEPT LINDA WHO WANTS YOU AND GRANT TO BREAK UP SO SHE CAN DATE HIM.

ALSO, YOU HAD A CALL FROM A CLIENT.

THANK YOU.

HE THINKS YOU'RE BEING PETTY AND THAT YOU SHOULD INVITE GRANT OVER FOR A NICE HOT DINNER.

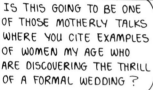

IS THIS GOING TO BE ONE OF THOSE MOTHERLY TALKS WHERE YOU CITE EXAMPLES OF WOMEN MY AGE WHO ARE DISCOVERING THE THRILL OF A FORMAL WEDDING?

NO.

OLDER WOMEN WHO REGRET NOT HAVING KIDS?

NO.

PROMISCUOUS WOMEN WHO REGRET BEING PROMISCUOUS?

NO.

DOES IT INVOLVE A DISEASE?

NOPE.

A DRUG?

NOPE.

A DEAR ABBY CLIPPING?

NOPE.

THEN **WHAT**?! WHAT IS IT??!

IT'S IMPORTANT FOR A MOTHER TO BUILD IN AN ELEMENT OF SUSPENSE.

YOU PROBABLY HAD SOME VERY GOOD REASON FOR NOT TELLING IRVING YOU WERE DATING ME, CATHY.

OF COURSE I DID, GRANT.

I WANTED TO EXPERIENCE THE THRILL OF DATING SOMEONE NEW WITHOUT JEOPARDIZING WHAT I HAD WITH HIM.

THEN IF NOTHING WORKS OUT WITH YOU I CAN GO RUNNING BACK TO IRVING WITHOUT HAVING HIM TORTURE ME ABOUT YOU FOR THE NEXT SIX MONTHS!

ISN'T IT WONDERFUL HOW YOUR PROBLEMS SOLVE THEMSELVES WHEN YOU TALK ABOUT THEM?!

I ATE A DONUT. AFTER-WARDS, I REALIZED MY URGE FOR THAT DONUT WAS JUST A MANIFESTATION OF MY JOB ANXIETY.

I ATE A BOX OF COOKIES. AFTERWARDS, I REALIZED THE COOKIES WERE JUST A SYMBOLIC COMPENSATION FOR MY INABILITY TO MAINTAIN A FULFILLING RELATIONSHIP.

I ATE A CARROT. I REALIZED NOTHING.

WHY DO I ONLY GET PHILOSOPHICAL AFTER I'VE EATEN SOMETHING FATTENING?

I HAVE 42 LETTERS TO GET OUT THIS MORNING, AND ALL I CAN THINK ABOUT IS THE DONUT I SAW ON CHARLENE'S DESK.

I GET AS FAR AS "DEAR MR. COOPER," AND THEN THAT DONUT POPS INTO MY MIND..... GET OUT OF MY MIND, DONUT!!

I AM IN CHARGE HERE!! YOU ARE NOT GOING TO RUN MY LIFE, YOU MISERABLE LITTLE DONUT!!

"DEAR MR. COOPER, REGARDING YOUR BUDGET, WE HAVE PAID SPECIAL ATTENTION TO THE LITTLE COLORED SPRINKLES ON THE THICK FUDGE FROSTING..."

HOW'S THE DIET, CATHY?

I HAD A BLUEBERRY MUFFIN ONE INCH FROM MY MOUTH, CHARLENE... BUT I RAN INTO THE BATHROOM AND THREW IT DOWN THE TOILET!

I HAD AN UNWRAPPED CANDY BAR IN MY HANDS... I CRUSHED IT TO PIECES AND THREW IT DOWN THE TOILET!!

I WAS SECONDS AWAY FROM A CHEESE DANISH! I SQUASHED IT WITH MY STAPLER AND THREW IT DOWN THE TOILET!!

THAT'S TERRIFIC, CATHY! LET ME KNOW IF THERE'S ANYTHING I CAN DO.

CALL MAINTENANCE.

TWO YEARS AGO YOU BOUGHT A JUMP ROPE. YOU SAID, "IF I'VE INVESTED $5, I'LL USE IT." YOU DIDN'T.

LAST YEAR YOU BOUGHT A SWEATSUIT AND A WORKOUT ALBUM. YOU SAID, "IF I'VE INVESTED $60, I'LL USE THEM." YOU DIDN'T.

NOW YOU'RE GOING TO BUY A $500 MEMBERSHIP IN A HEALTH CLUB?? CATHY, WHAT ARE YOU THINKING??

THE OLDER I GET, THE MORE IT COSTS TO MAKE ME FEEL GUILTY.

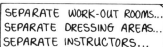

OH, YES. OUR HEALTH CLUB HAS COMPLETELY SEPARATE FACILITIES FOR MEN AND WOMEN.

WONDERFUL.

SEPARATE WORK-OUT ROOMS... SEPARATE DRESSING AREAS... SEPARATE INSTRUCTORS...

WONDERFUL.

ANY OTHER QUESTIONS?

HOW AM I SUPPOSED TO GET IN THE FRONT DOOR?

HEALTH CLUB

CATHY, HOW DID YOU LOSE 10 POUNDS IN 4 DAYS??

NEW FAT IS EASIER TO LOSE THAN OLD FAT, ANDREA.

IT'S ALL TIMING. IF YOU GAIN 5 POUNDS IN ONE NIGHT, YOU COULD LOSE IT IN 2 DAYS. BUT IF YOU WAIT A WEEK, FORGET IT.

AFTER A WEEK, THE NEW FAT HAS ALREADY BECOME PART OF YOUR BODY'S FAT FAMILY AND IT'S...

...SOMETIMES I HATE THE THINGS I'M AN EXPERT ON.

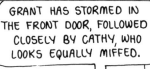

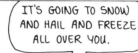

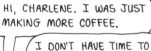

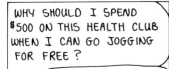

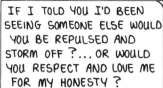

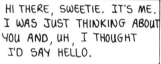

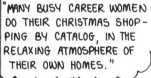

A PRACTICAL GIFT TELLS HIM THE ROMANCE IS OVER. A PERSONAL GIFT TELLS HIM THE ROMANCE HAS JUST BEGUN.

AN INTIMATE GIFT SAYS YOU WANT TO GET CLOSER. A KITCHEN GIFT SAYS YOU WANT HIM TO CHANGE. A SPORTS GIFT SAYS YOU WANT HIM TO THINK YOU UNDERSTAND HIM.

A HAND-MADE GIFT SAYS, "I'M SWEET AND HOMEY"... AN EXPENSIVE GIFT SAYS, "I'M INDEPENDENT AND WORLDLY AND AWARE!!"

WHAT DID YOU DECIDE TO GET IRVING?

THE GIFT OF CONFUSION.

AS EACH GIFT IS OPENED, FATHER WILL NEATLY FOLD THE GIFT WRAP FOR RE-USE, AND I WILL RECORD WHO EACH PRESENT IS FROM SO WE'LL HAVE A COMPLETE LIST FOR OUR THANK YOU NOTES!

...NOT BAD. AT LEAST THIS YEAR I HAD TIME TO GET MY WHOLE SPEECH OUT.

MORE PIE? MORE COOKIES? MORE STRUDEL? MORE NUT BREAD? MORE CANDY?

THERE ARE DEEP, PSYCHOLOGICAL REASONS FOR WHY MOTHERS STUFF THEIR CHILDREN WITH FOOD OVER THE HOLIDAYS, MOM.

I KNOW, CATHY.

IF I FATTEN YOU UP, YOU'LL BE TOO EMBARRASSED TO LEAVE THE HOUSE, SO YOU'LL STAY LONGER!

...SO MUCH FOR INTROSPECTION.

...AND LASTLY, I WILL NEVER AGAIN THROW DRIED-OUT PENS BACK IN MY DESK DRAWER!

SUGAR

GOOD FOR YOU, CATHY.

BY MAKING A SMALL NEW YEAR'S RESOLUTION THAT YOU **KNOW** YOU CAN KEEP, YOU'LL GAIN THE CONFIDENCE YOU NEED TO STICK TO YOUR BIG RESOLUTION!!

THAT **WAS** MY BIG RESOLUTION.

I REMEMBER THAT SONG! THAT WAS #1 THE DAY I OVERSLEPT AND RAN INTO THE DRAPE MEETING WITH HOT ROLLERS IN MY HAIR!

OH, AND THAT ONE...THAT WAS #1 THE DAY I GOT STUCK IN TRAFFIC, CAUSING 16 SERVINGS OF "LASAGNA FOR ONE" TO THAW PREMATURELY IN MY TRUNK!

OH, WAIT! HERE'S MY FAVORITE! THIS SONG HIT #1 THE DAY THAT EVERY MECHANICAL, ELECTRICAL AND DIGITAL THING I OWN BLEW UP WITHIN TEN MINUTES OF EACH OTHER!!

I CAN'T BELIEVE THIS, CATHY.

I KNOW. 1982'S GOING TO BE HARD TO TOP.

ARE YOU STILL ADMIRING THAT THING?

THERE'S NOTHING IN THE WORLD LIKE A NEW CALENDAR, CHARLENE.

THINK OF THE HISTORY THAT WILL UNFOLD ON THESE PAGES! I WILL RECORD EVERY ACCOMPLISHMENT! EVERY TRIUMPH!!

CATHY, IT'S 10:45!!

"MONDAY, JAN. 3, 1983: MISSED THE STYLECRAFT MEETING BY TWO HOURS."

WE HAVE THE AUTO-REDIAL TELEPHONE WITH 9, 15, OR 32-NUMBER MEMORY... THE ALL-ELECTRONIC MINI-PHONE... CORDLESS, COLLAPSIBLE OR CALCULATOR PHONES...

PHONES WITH A MUTE SWITCH, RINGER ON/OFF SWITCH, AND/OR AMPLIFIER SWITCH. PHONES THAT WILL ANSWER, RECORD, TIME CALLS OR TURN ELECTRICAL APPLIANCES ON OR OFF FROM ANYWHERE IN THE WORLD!

DO YOU HAVE ANY PHONES THAT WILL NOT RING SO MUCH AT THE OFFICE, BUT WILL RING MORE AT HOME?

NO.

ONCE AGAIN, MODERN TECHNOLOGY ZOOMS PAST THE OBVIOUS.

PHONE CENTER

WHAT HAPPENED HERE?!

I STUFFED MY PHONE BILL DOWN THE GARBAGE DISPOSAL AND IT BROKE.

THAT WILL BE $42.00.

$42.00?? BLAAAA!!

RIP!!

APARTMENT 365: HOME OF THE DAILY COMPOUNDED DEBT.

YOU SEEM TO INTUITIVELY KNOW HOW TO HANDLE THE OZWELL CLIENT, CATHY. PLEASE CALL AND EXPLAIN WHY WE'RE $12,000.00 OVER BUDGET.

I HAVE ALWAYS FOUGHT FOR WOMEN'S RIGHTS. WANT TO COME OVER AND SEE MY FILE OF CORRESPONDENCE WITH PRO-WOMAN LEGISLATORS??

I LOVE AND RESPECT YOU ENOUGH TO KNOW YOU NEED TIME TO YOURSELF, MY DARLING. BYE.

MEN ARE REALLY STARTING TO CHANGE, AREN'T THEY?

YES. THEY'RE GETTING SNEAKIER.

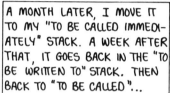

REMEMBER WHEN WE USED TO CRUISE THIS MALL AND CHECK OUT THE LADIES, IRVING?

DON'T TORTURE ME, ZACK.

WHAT WOMAN IS GOING TO LOOK AT A COUPLE OF GUYS WITH A 2-YEAR-OLD?

A BABY! A BABY!!

LET ME HOLD HER.

IT USED TO BE ALL A GUY NEEDED TO ATTRACT THE LADIES WAS A SPORTS CAR. I COULD HANDLE THAT.

THEN PLANTS. A GUY WITH A FICUS BENJIMINA AND A $2,000 STEREO SYSTEM HAD IT MADE.

APT 300

...BUT NOW I DON'T SEEM "WITH IT" UNLESS I HAVE A 2-YEAR-OLD AND A BRIEF-CASE FULL OF TOYS. CATHY, HOW AM I SUPPOSED TO DO THAT??!

OH, IRVING...

PATHOS. THE UNIVERSAL CHARMER.

IN MODERN PARENTING, WE LEARN THAT A CHILD'S ACTIONS ARE ALWAYS MOTIVATED, IRVING.

SPLAT!

BECKY SENSES YOUR HOSTILITY TOWARDS HER, AND IS EXPRESSING HER FRUSTRATION BY THROWING FOOD AT YOU.

SPLAT!

I SEE BECKY'S IN THE FOOD-FLINGING STAGE.

ALSO A POSSIBILITY.

I BOUGHT A $90 DRESS FOR DINNER WITH IRVING TONIGHT.

I BOUGHT $20 PERFUME TO SMELL BEAUTIFUL FOR IRVING, AND $7 MASCARA SO I CAN GAZE MEANINGFULLY INTO IRVING'S EYES!

THIS YEAR, I'M GOING TO KEEP IRVING FASCINATED THROUGH FEBRUARY 14!!

YOU SPENT $117 TO KEEP IRVING FASCINATED THROUGH FEBRUARY 14??

I DIDN'T WANT TO WASTE THE 85¢ I SPENT ON HIS VALENTINE.

7:30... I STRIKE MY SULTRY, COME-HITHER POSE.

8:05... I STRIKE MY TOTALLY MIFFED POSE.

8:27... I STRIKE MY HOSTILITY POSE... NO. TOO MEAN... I STRIKE MY EMPATHY POSE... NO. TOO NICE... I STRIKE MY..

HI, CATHY. SORRY I'M SO LATE.

I'M NOT READY YET.

I LOOKED AT ALL THE VALENTINE'S DAY CARDS AND CANDY AND JEWELRY, HONEY...

...BUT NOTHING WAS LOVELY ENOUGH TO EXPRESS MY FEELINGS FOR YOU ON THIS MOST MEANINGFUL OCCASION.

OH.. WELL...

BONK!

AS WE GET OLDER, WE LEARN TO BE MORE DIRECT.

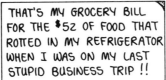

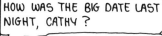
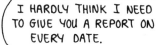

Panel 1: WE ASSERTED OUR INDEPENDENCE IN TIGHT, STRAIGHT SKIRTS AND BUTTONED VESTS.

Panel 2: WE REAFFIRMED OUR FEMININITY IN MINI-SKIRTS AND SEE-THROUGH TOPS.

Panel 3: NOW WE ARE SALUTING OUR INDEPENDENT YET FEMININE HEALTHY BODIES IN DAZZLING LEOTARDS AND TIGHTS.

Panel 4: EVERY TIME WOMEN ENTER ANOTHER PHASE, THERE'S A WHOLE NEW CATEGORY OF CLOTHES I CAN'T GET INTO.

Panel 5: BUTTON UP YOUR BLOUSE, SWEETIE. YOU DON'T WANT TO GIVE THE WRONG IMPRESSION. / OH, FOR HEAVEN'S SAKE, MOTHER. THIS IS 1983.

Panel 6: NEVER BE PUSHY. PUSHY WOMEN ARE VERY UNATTRACTIVE. / MOM, THIS IS BUSINESS. I **HAVE** TO BE PUSHY TO GET AHEAD.

Panel 7: PUT THE ROLL DOWN, DEAR. YOU HAVE POTATOES COMING WITH YOUR MEAL. / THERE IS NOTHING WRONG WITH ONE ROLL.

Panel 8: CATHY! I CAN'T BELIEVE A WHOLE WEEK HAS SLIPPED BY SINCE I TALKED TO YOU! / NEITHER CAN I, MOM...

Panel 9: SHAMPOO I TRIED ONCE AND HATED...COLOGNE I'VE GOTTEN SICK OF...FACE CREAM THAT DIDN'T WORK...

Panel 10: MAKEUP THAT'S THE WRONG COLOR...HAIR CLIPS THAT WON'T STAY IN MY HAIR...BUBBLE BATH THAT I'M ALLERGIC TO...

Panel 11: MY BATHROOM CUPBOARDS ARE FILLED WITH THINGS I WILL NEVER USE, FORCING ME TO THROW THE THINGS I **DO** USE ALL OVER THE COUNTER!

Panel 12: THE FAMILY TRADITION LIVES ON!!

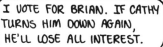

MY FRIEND FLO'S DAUGHTER'S EX-ROOMMATE SAW CATHY HAVING DINNER WITH IRVING TONIGHT AND CATHY DID NOT LOOK HAPPY.

FLO CALLED THE JOHNSTON FAMILY, WHO ALERTED LOUISE, WHO CALLED MARTHA, WHO CALLED JOAN, WHO WIRED SUSAN, WHO FINALLY TRACKED ME DOWN AT THE MARKET...

CATHY, SWEETIE... TELL YOUR MOTHER WHAT'S WRONG !!

MOM ! HOW DID YOU KNOW ??

SOME DAYS MOTHERLY INTUITION TAKES MORE OF US THAN OTHERS.

WHAT SHOULD I SAY IF IRVING ASKS ME OUT ?

IF HE ASKS YOU OUT FOR FRIDAY NIGHT, IT MEANS YOU'RE SECOND CHOICE. TELL HIM NO.

IF HE ASKS YOU OUT FOR SATURDAY NIGHT, IT MEANS HE PROBABLY JUST BROKE UP WITH SOMEONE AND WILL TRY TO MOLD YOU INTO HIS EX-GIRLFRIEND. TELL HIM NO.

ALL THE "WINNERS" OF FRIDAY AND SATURDAY NIGHT GET DISPLAYED AT SUNDAY BRUNCH. IF HE ASKS YOU OUT FOR SUNDAY BRUNCH, TELL HIM NO !

...SUDDENLY, I'M STARTING TO WISH IT WAS MONDAY.

ANGER EVENTUALLY PASSES. FRUSTRATION GOES AWAY. EVEN LOVE CAN DISAPPEAR.

WHY IS IT THAT ONLY EM-BARRASSMENT STAYS EXACT-LY AS INTENSE FIVE YEARS LATER AS IT WAS THE MOMENT YOU WERE FIRST EMBARRAS-SED ABOUT SOMETHING ??!

...AND WHY DO I KEEP RE-PROVING THAT THEORY ?